ALPACA
REVISITED

by H. L. Hunt

HLH PRODUCTS • DALLAS, TEXAS

CONTENTS

CHAPTER 1

JUAN ACHALA BEGINS A SEARCH

Juan Achala was leaving home — leaving the land of his birth, and although he had some knowledge of the outside world and liked to think of himself as sophisticated, Alpaca was the only home he had ever known. He gazed with feeling at the receding shoreline of the country from which he was fleeing. His departure from Alpaca was in the nature of an exile, although it was really self-imposed. He was leaving behind him in the little six-province nation an evil spectre of dictatorship. He loathed the present dictator and his rule, just as he had loathed the preceding "strong man" usurpers who had followed one another in Alpaca in agonizing, rapid succession. From the stern rail of the well-appointed ship, he looked back in deep reflection. He wanted to get as far away as possible from the chatter of fellow passengers. He needed time to think. Always he pondered the troubled past and inscrutable future of his unhappy country, where peace had seldom been known.

Moreover, he felt a strong and driving conviction that he must not only think about lasting peace but that he must do everything to attain it. What Alpaca needed was a new political plan and a new purpose, but in the agonized urgency of the day-to-day crises, no one had seemed to have the perspective and the long view to find a way out. Perhaps it was bold of him to believe that he could succeed where others had failed, but he was resolved to make the attempt.

He had made up his mind that he would go out into the world centers of thought and culture and seek a cure for Alpaca's political plight.

He planned to visit Paris, Jerusalem, Geneva, Roma, Athens and other historic seats of European culture. In these centers, he would talk with thoughtful men who had studied the problems of government, both past and present, and he would get their viewpoints. He would not confine himself to scholars, but would talk with students, merchants and people in all walks of life, and endeavor to learn their thoughts and reactions to his opinions. He was searching for the truths that would enable him to conceive an effective plan which would make dictatorship outmoded and, in fact, impossible in Alpaca. He knew that dictatorships, wherever set up, offer no future for any country nor even for themselves. Dictators, whether benevolent or evil, have no feasible plan for their peaceful succession. They are a fearsome juggernaut of force which has no place and is going nowhere in the field of a better world. He knew that all of them, including the greatest, at their end had become a deep and dark travesty racked by the fierce struggle for power which must follow in their wake.

Much family discussion had preceded his departure, taken without the fanfare which would have come with public announcement. Finances were ample for carefully planned expenditures. In his mind was the intriguing thought that his research might result in a definite plan for his country which would replace the intolerable dictatorship with a workable, balanced and efficient form of government, suited to the needs and temperament of the Alpacan people. It was an ambitious thought, but he was determined to pursue it with the best efforts at his command.

Ruby and opal lights from the sunset quivered on wind-vexed waves, gilding the distant roofs and towers, pointing up the green of trees and terraces, casting purple shadows against walls creamy white and pastel hued. Far inland he could still pick out those familiar mountain retreats where he had passed many hours respectfully listening to the eldest and wisest. They had talked always of the power and ways of government, contrasting and comparing the experiences of tribes, monarchies, democracies, republics and dictatorships with one another, and those of the dead past with those of the vibrant present. Such was the consuming interest, almost the obsession, of the Achalas of Alpaca and their close-knit circle.

Juan had absorbed their beliefs and misgivings from his earliest years. It was as natural for him to join in these political discussions as it was to bathe in the icy mountain streams or to swim in the warm surf or to ride the high-spirited horses for which Alpaca was renowned. Although he enjoyed the company of thinkers and sages, he could also be at home with the lonely shepherds while he hunted wild game, or when in the small cities, relaxed with his kind in sports and dances which marked the forgetting of care.

Upon one thing there was general agreement among his mentors. They believed that wise, fair government for the people, with prudent use of the natural resources allocated to mankind by a kindly Providence, was the supreme responsibility of thinking minds and willing hands.

Juan's marked aptitude was quickly noted and encouraged. His youthful enthusiasm and splendid caution were counted a bright hope for his country's future. There had been times in the past when Alpaca had been nominally free with an uneasy kind of freedom but lasting peace had always been elusive and a phantom goal.

He leaned against the rail and thought unhappily: Would it have been better had he insisted on remaining in Alpaca at this crucial period in his country's history? If he had, he might have incurred only minor personal inconveniences and indignities, yet who could tell? Such a course, he told himself, would have been a poor substitute for the mission which had become a burning cause in his life. He was familiar with conventional weapons and could handle them well, but none thought the situation could be saved by violence. He felt that his parents, at robust middle age, were mutually self-sufficient, hence would not miss him unduly; and they were under no more than the usual stress and strain of life in Alpaca. It had been agreed that they would keep him informed of happenings and, should need arise, he could quickly return.

Having abruptly severed home ties, Juan felt a deep longing for the irrecoverable past. Several passengers were eyeing him with unconcealed curiosity. A quick glance revealed all were unknown to him. What he did not realize was that his proud athletic bearing, his air of inborn courtesy unmarred by hauteur, his flashing eyes beneath shapely brows, and his magnificent even white teeth, accenting a ready smile, exerted a magnetic attraction even upon strangers. Perhaps he was to become more aware of his innate persuasiveness and power, as he voyaged far to encounter people and conditions, new and exciting.

That destiny can play amazing tricks, he knew. He had burning convictions but there were few in Alpaca, he told himself, who could agree with him. That there might be more than a few beckoning in the wide world was his fond hope. He felt a deep yearning to find one, only one, truly sympathetic soul preferably of his age and station. Would he ever find that one? He had warm friends, but had they ever fully understood the dire need for a better life in Alpaca? And if they did, would they stand with him or would they soon lose heart, relapse into easy leisure, and succumb to blandishments?

The young men he knew best tended to be more opinionated than profound; energetic, never idle, but always working, playing or fighting with equal abandon. They were immature, emotional and lovable, often gay, more often sad, without quite knowing why. Their faces passed before him in a montage of favorable and faulty traits. None of them seemed to fit into the time and place his imagination had carved. As for girls, he had found them congenial companions for his lighter hours — gay and friendly, nothing more; lovely today, forgotten tomorrow.

Juan assumed that Alpacans were typical of people generally throughout the world. He did not feel provincial, although he was as yet untraveled and untouched by great world events, but he had a never-ending feeling that government and public affairs as he had known them were needlessly bad and somehow, sometime, there must be better days ahead for Alpaca. But first . . . there must be Peace! Nearly everyone wanted peace. He believed people could attain peace if they were permitted to govern themselves.

Juan had an uncanny grasp of nearly all that went on around him; what he could not see or hear, he sensed. He was even more intuitive than women are thought to be. However, he did not trust his intuition very far. He was more logical than mystic, utterly realistic; imaginative, yet down to earth. He longed to be fully competent, ready to meet any emergency. His tutors liked him and had termed him superior. He had read widely, knew history written and traditional. He excelled in languages, geometry and logic; had a bowing acquaintance with abstract philosophy; was receptive to new ideas but required they stand up under penetrating analysis.

He now entertained no premonition of troubles or perplexities he might encounter in his travels. He would meet the problems as they arose.

When he tried to review his beliefs, Juan had to recognize that they were hard to analyze and classify. Perhaps that was why older men, who frankly expected much from him in the future, had urged this trip. Although by nature joyous, he at times felt turmoil, dissatisfaction and uncertainty within himself. He believed strongly in achievement by individual man, of his own potential, before mass man could hope to establish Liberty, Justice, and Peace.

In the deepening dusk he suddenly decided this was a good time to take a brisk walk on deck and breathe deeply of the sea air. Air was free and epitomized a spirit of freedom and peace which had come to mean everything to Juan. Not many people were about. After a few turns he paused at the rail.

With the resilience of youth, he could breathe in the starlit beauty of the sea and enjoy the breeze which now had freshened. All at once he was aware of a presence. A girl was standing not far away but he, preoccupied, paid little attention. Vaguely conscious of soft footsteps, he was slightly startled when she said "Achala?" It was as if she asked a question. Her voice was caressing, with rich overtones. In the dim light, her white dress gleamed. With queenly gesture she drew a lacy scarf closer around her shoulders. He said very formally:

"I am happy to admit that I am of the Achala family" — and waited for her to tell who she was but she did not supply the name of her clan.

"Alpaca is my home too," she remarked, "although I am seldom there." Her voice had that tantalizing warm quality, with the sweetness of a Strad in the hands of a master. She added casually: "They call me Mara."

"An expatriate?" he said lightly.

"No, no. A student — Vienna, Milano and now Paris."

"Music?" he ventured.

"Ah," she replied. "You are very astute."

"Do we know each other?" He wished the light were not so dim. Laughing deliciously, she said teasingly: "That is where I have the advantage of you. I know you but you do not know me. At least, probably not."

He longed to ask her last name but decided she would tell him if she wanted him to know. After all, proper young ladies of Alpaca, even though they had lived abroad, did not ordinarily introduce themselves to strangers on shipboard. They exchanged the names of European capitals, all of which she seemed to know, and where he hoped to visit.

"Are you interested in government?" he asked after awhile.

"Oh, government?" she said with a hint of boredom. "You mean politics."

"You might say," he answered seriously, "that politics is the gateway into government."

"Into government good or bad," she retorted with a perception that intrigued him. "No, I can't say I've had time to think much about it. But the men in my family do."

Again he longed to ask who they were. What was their philosophy? — or which side were they on? She evidently had no desire to tell. Was she indifferent, playful, or hostile? He had no lead whatever. She was, he decided, a good little actress.

"What do you think of woman suffrage?" he asked.

Her answer was as he expected but unnecessarily vehement, he thought. "Women should have the ballot — we will have, when voting which is counted comes to our land — we certainly share man's responsibilty."

"I suppose you wouldn't be old enough to vote," he ventured.

"That would depend," she said demurely, "on the laws of the country where I resided."

Neatly expressed, Juan thought; but made no comment, except: "I'm sure I've heard your voice somewhere. It's a voice one could never forget."

"Indeed?" said she archly. "That's possible."

They were silent for a minute, and she hummed a few bars from Violetta's big aria in the first act of *La Traviata* but cut it off immediately, observing "I must go in. My aunt always travels with me. She will be looking for me, telling me not to risk the night air. Pooh! Night air is the best kind."

"Of course it is," he agreed immediately. "Couldn't we take a stroll on the deck?"

"Not this evening, thank you," she said positively. "We may meet again." And then, impulsively, "I have admired you from a distance, Achala, for a long time. Will you make me a promise?"

"Of course," he said recklessly. "What is it, fair lady?"

She leaned over, very close in the starlit gloom, and whispered, "Just don't forget me, that's all. There are other things than politics."

In an instant, she had brushed past him and was gone. But her lacy scarf, delicate as a whisper, was in his hand. It breathed a perfume of rose and jasmine; the episode caused his heart, his impervious heart, to skip a beat. He laughed softly. "The little flirt!" Juan said under his breath, "I'll see her in the morning, by daylight. Jove, is she demure? Or is she Parisienne?" He wasn't quite sure whether or not he would return her bit of gossamer scarf. Meanwhile, he folded it over and over and placed it in an inside pocket, marveling at its amazing lightness and lack of bulk.

But the next morning Juan, or "Achala" as he had overnight begun thinking of himself, having been sufficiently enthralled to look forward eagerly to meeting Mara and assessing her visible charms, learned with surprise that she and her traveling companion had disembarked at the first port of call at an early hour of the morning. He was stunned. Their visit had been brief and fragmentary, yet he was impressed and mystified.

"She knew it all the time," Achala said to himself in mingled anger and amusement. "Why didn't she give me her name? Oh, well, there aren't many families in Alpaca that harbor such daughters — I'll probably be able to place her soon." And he racked his memory for the answer, but it evaded him. She might belong to some household of the opposition — yet no, she believed in suffrage, woman suffrage at that; such was not a mark of the oppressive government in power. That she had led a life of luxury he was inclined to guess. But, she was a student, hence of some serious inclination. What branch of music could be her *forte?* That voice — that vibrant voice! Singing, without doubt. How stupid he had been. Singing — would it be opera? The snatch from *La Traviata* — where had he heard that, lately?

Of a sudden it came to him. An enchanting soloist. It could have been, must have been, this stately girl. What was her name? Busy with some issue of State, he had paid little heed. But he could find out who she was. And possibly — his pulse quickened — possibly they would meet again, in Paris.

CHAPTER 2

LESSONS IN EUROPE

Roma was Achala's first stop. Here he was to confer with the internationally renowned lawyer, Orlando Tasso. This contact had been arranged by Juan's uncle. The two had been students together at Heidelberg years ago, shortly before the outbreak of World War I. Orlando Tasso was a law student while Juan's uncle was studying medicine. Both had passionate interest in sociology and government. During the intervening years, they had pursued successful careers in their specialized fields while ever keeping close and often deeply-disturbed watch on the progress of world affairs, by correspondence and by occasional exchange of visits, though these were but brief intervals snatched from busy lives. Juan could remember having met the revered Tasso, in early youth; but of personal intimacy there had been none, owing to disparity in ages. Now, however, Achala hoped he was of sufficient maturity to share ideas and to learn much.

"You may find," said the great Orlando, at their first interview, "that the language barrier still exists for you in Europe despite the careful tutoring you have had. Tell me, how does it seem to you, to hear Italian spoken all about you, instead of translating it in a classroom?"

"I read your language, sir, with ease," replied Achala. "Conversation is not too difficult when it comes slowly and distinctly, as you have been speaking. But to catch the flood of rapidly-spoken idiom heard in general, makes me think that I would need several months of concentrated attention to the language alone, to become fluent and re-laxed in it."

"That is very true," said Tasso in French. "Is this tongue easier for you?"

"Oh, yes sir," said Achala in relief. "I have carried on

conversation with native French teachers and members of my family, since I can remember."

"Good, good! my boy — I observe your French accent is better than mine."

"Thank you, sir," said Achala modestly.

"How is your command of English?"

"I find it easy to speak and understand," said Achala in English, "but difficult to write, with its confused spelling. At home we employ English a great deal because of its widespread use throughout the world."

"You have been well taught," said the elder man. "Italian is for poetry, French for diplomacy, German and Swedish for science, Spanish and English for commerce, English for law, history, political science — and general convenience.

"Your uncle has of course informed me that you are one of a group centered on saving your land of Alpaca from the grasp of the spoilers. I agree that this is the noblest work you could embrace. No man of conscience wishes to see civilization dethroned. And it is commendable to try to save your own country from ruin, rather than launch out with wild, unrestrained ambitions, which in the end will subjugate, tyrannize, and enslave."

"It seems to me, sir," said Achala, trying not to be over-bold, "that we must begin with the individual before we can benefit society, which consists of individuals. And the crux of all that, I can't help thinking, is the protection of the individual's mind from becoming slanted toward acceptance of totalitarian government and from the great danger of having his mentality arrested or destroyed completely, not only by sly propaganda, but by the evil drugs and psychic pressures of unscrupulous despots."

Tasso's lined face saddened. "That is truly the crux of the matter, and we who would avert the danger must lose no time on abstractions for the time to resist dictatorship is short. Concrete measures are a stern need. What have your enlightened leaders worked out?"

Achala opened his briefcase, took out a meager sheaf of papers carefully prepared, containing the accumulated political wisdom of the Achala clan.

"Here is a synopsis of our labors to date," he said. "But we are merely groping. It is not we who are the leaders. That is what we would like to be. If we are unduly aggressive, we shall be accused of self-seeking and of power madness. You say the time to resist dictatorship is short. How can we step out and try to destroy it quickly without forfeiting the very thing we value the most — peace with order?"

"Such indeed is the problem," said Tasso, as he glanced through the pages. "I will retain this for further study. It appears to me that your self-appointed task is threefold. First, to formulate a comprehensive charter, or constitution, for national government. Second, to get it adopted without internal revolution. Third, to make it work, to the people's advantage."

"Correct, sir."

"I suggest that you devote what time you have in Roma to intensive study of law and government, and the history of both, in my library. I will select books for you, and since time is a factor, will mark the pertinent passages. You need more background than you now have, I believe. I will then discuss the points with you. It will be a sort of seminar with the nephew of my old friend. Ah, what times we had together in Heidelberg, in the old days!" His eyes sparkled with unspoken memories and Achala, feeling sure that sparkling ladies contributed to those memories, was instantly reminded of Mara, whose indistinct image lingered in his thoughts and whose melodious voice still echoed in his memory. Realizing that this first interview was ended, he expressed his thanks and made his farewells. He returned to his hotel carrying several books of reference, greatly encouraged by the progress and prospects.

At the same time, in a pleasant Paris apartment which was dominated by a grand piano and strewn with operatic scores, a beautiful, exotic young lady was brushing her cloud of lovely hair and watching her aunt unpack the trunks and bags.

"I told you, Aunt Arifa, I did not *want* to leave the boat. I preferred to come straight through, as we had planned."

"And I preferred to keep my word to your father and mother," replied the aunt firmly, "to prevent interruptions in your studies, at least until you have made your debut in Milano. A fortune has already been spent on your career, young lady. We do not propose to see you deflected."

"Deflected, my foot!" exclaimed Mara inelegantly. "Can't I even get acquainted with the most attractive young man of Alpaca?"

"Not when it might lead to complications of the most involved nature," said Arifa calmly, as she deftly folded nylons. "Ever since you were ten years old you've been trying to throw yourself at the head of that radical Juan Achala. I know his type. He is romantic. You are romantic. 'Get her off the boat,' your father would have said, 'if you have to swim for the shore.' Don't think I wasn't watching you, young lady. I saw the play you made for Achala at your very first chance. Fortunately it was so dark, I don't think he would recognize you again."

"But I would recognize him," said Mara triumphantly. "And I shall see him again, I promise you. Next time, things will be different."

"There will be no next time. You know what happens if you disobey me. Your allowance will be completely cut off, all these expensive lessons in ballet and opera will be ended, and your debut at La Scala will be canceled. You will be thrown penniless upon the world, with no future, no friends. I am here to keep you from doing something foolish that you will regret your life long. Achala is not for you. Achala is poison to the government in Alpaca, and unacceptable to the honored family of Hani."

"Achala is an honored family, too," protested Mara Hani. "Achala men are distinguished. Achala women are noble, beautiful, good and kind."

"What foolishness, child! I tell you they are on the other side. The Hani women are gentlewomen. I was ashamed when you told him that you embraced the shocking notion of votes for women, which of course would mean participation in politics, dirty politics. Most unladylike."

"Why should politics always be dirty?" Mara wanted to know. "Can't it ever take a bath?"

"Now you're being witty," said her aunt, laughing and hugging her. "That's my sweet, brilliant girl, who will soon be ready to enter upon an operatic career and become the despair and envy of all the ladies, the toast of all the gentlemen. Come now, practice trills and cadenzas for thirty minutes. I will play your accompaniment, and then your fencing master will be waiting for you. Oh, my precious darling, can't you see that all we Hanis are doing is entirely for your own good?"

"I do like to sing," admitted Mara. "And I like to make an audience stand up and cheer. Stage emotions, though, are not enough. There must be a few real emotions, too."

"Plenty of time for that," said Arifa. "You'll be a sensation, my love, if you will only keep your head, not let your heart betray you into making inferior connections."

Mara murmured rebelliously, "Achala is not inferior — if ever you say that again, I'll cancel the debut myself! So there!"

CHAPTER 3

REUNION WITH MARA

As soon as Achala reached Geneva, he found available to him the sources of information about which he had been dreaming. His first rude awakening about the governments he had exalted came when he found that Switzerland and Uruguay, which had often been held up to him as near-perfect forms of government, had probably endured only because of peculiar situations which favored the inhabitants and lands of those countries, rather than from any profound wisdom in the plan of their governments.

He soon decided the Swiss had succeeded in staying out of two World Wars, not because of their own wisdom, but because the belligerents had valued Switzerland more as a neutral than as a participant. Almost any of them could at one time or another easily have invaded and subjugated that little country. He was struck by the thought: "Will they only leave Alpaca alone if we get freedom started there, as they have the Swiss?"

Achala's contacts were excellent. Everywhere he was well received. He occupied himself each day with the accumulation and storing of ideas, sometimes visiting or working far into the night. He could simply find no one whose ideas he did not want to explore, so long as they could make even the slightest contribution to his subject of government. Busy as he was, he found himself thinking more and more about Mara and the caress in her voice when she first addressed him as Achala. He found himself wondering what Mara was doing and what she would think of some aspect or situation in the life of nations with which he was engrossed. In her absence he built up a high regard for her opinions. It came as a shock to him that he knew little or nothing about her views aside from the fact that she ardently favored woman suffrage.

Did this dearth of information prevent the bemused young

man from continuing to create an ideal portrait of Mara? Of course not! He dreamed up a paragon such as hardly any human being could ever bring to life. Without being an ardent patron of the arts, he shrewdly surmised that no young woman would be advised to pursue an operatic career unless she had great talent, poise, perseverance, charm, beauty of face and figure. Out of whole cloth, because he needed desperately to believe it, he endowed her with common sense and the capacity for sympathetically understanding Alpaca's political conditions. Had he not thrown in those desirable traits for good measure, Achala could hardly have survived the weeks which must elapse before his itinerary would bring him to Paris.

When his mail caught up with him, he received copies of home newspapers. In them he found a flattering item about an opera singer recently returned to her studies in Europe. Her name, he learned, was Mlle. Mara Hani. This news amazed him. The Hani family, very prominent in his native land, was thought to be tolerant of the dictatorship transiently in power, although not openly allied with the government despised by the Achalas. The report identified Mara — but otherwise it was distasteful.

The Hanis were a commercial family interested in shipping, agriculture and industrial projects on a large scale. They believed in getting along with the "powers that be," however and wherever they found them.

The Achalas, on the contrary, were idealists imbued with thoughts for promoting freedom and individual liberty; moderately wealthy and entirely aloof from those "inside deals" which the unscrupulous often carried on. The Hanis never soiled their hands with open political moves, whereas the Achalas would risk censure, public abuse and smears for the sake of conscience.

It was a delicate situation, intolerable to him, and Achala swallowed hard. He did not for one moment associate Mara with anything ignoble. His idealization of her would not permit the intrusion of one unkind thought. No! She was a victim of circumstances, from which, when the time came, he must rescue her. The lace scarf which he treasured became an emblem of all that was fine and fragile, beautiful and womanly, in sympathy and accord with his own strivings. Mara Hani — what a beautiful name! Because she bore it, he must not castigate the tribe of Hani. There must be some good in them, to have produced so perfect a flower.

Achala found himself making excuses for hastening to Paris. In addition to the study of government which Paris would offer, there was a lingering, yearning hope that he might there find the beautiful Mara Hani.

In Roma and Geneva, Achala made many friends who lived in those cities, as well as new-found friends who were, like Achala, visitors there. They quickly became interested in his search for facts to build a plan for a government in the future. Wherever he had been, friends he made from London, The Hague, Athens, Paris and other centers represented the most inspiring future contacts for him in their homelands.

Achala wrote fluently and some of his young friends, learning of his burning and consuming desire to originate a workable constitution for his small country, volunteered their best efforts, training and secretarial talents to the cause. Some were historians of parts — some could write clearly, many had vast experience — all could think; soon there was a group.

In Paris he had some marginal time — as what young man in Paris would not? — and within a few days his close attention to newspapers and billboards was rewarded. The talented and glamorous Mara Hani, coloratura soprano, longtime student under Francois Rochelle and other maestros, would sing an aria on a charity program at the Palace of Baron and Baroness Brumaire, on Tuesday evening, just one month prior to her scheduled operatic debut in *Lucia di*

Lammermoor, at the world-famed La Scala, in Milano. Tickets were available at a certain office and for a certain fancy price.

Achala found out that this was a top social event of the season, and that the international titled set would be well represented. Tuesday evening found him properly attired and occupying a box seat in the intimate, gilded private recital hall of the Brumaire Palace, which dated back to the time when Haydn and Mozart were proteges of royalty, and performed at the royal beck and call. The box seated six — he had bought the last ticket. Not certain whether or not he should introduce himself to the other five occupants, who seemed to be close friends, he contented himself with acknowledging their presence by bowing and smiling. This apparently was acceptable decorum. Achala still did not know that his presence was magnetic, and in any company of notables he fitted like hand in glove. He settled back in the outside chair of the rear row and prepared to endure the rest of the program until Mara should appear. She was billed to come last. The evening was endless.

During the program, consisting chiefly of intricate dances, he heard the ladies and gentlemen nearby discussing the ravishing new coloratura whom nobody knew, but of whom everyone had heard. She was said to be a meteor scintillating across the musical sky. She was said to be a mysterious princess from Egypt, appearing incognito, for reasons of State. It was asserted that La Scala was already sold out for the night of her forthcoming debut. It was rumored that all her diamonds were real; she would not wear rhinestones even to rehearsal. It was more or less reliably said that more than one prince had tried in vain to win her favor. All the gentlemen were on the *qui vive,* while the ladies fanned themselves languidly.

When at long last the dancers had danced every conceivable figure from adagio to tarantella, from cakewalk to tango, and had tirelessly taken their encores, a soft rustle of expectation and subdued excitement swept through the house; it was time for the fairytale singer to perform. The small orchestra in the miniature pit laid scores on racks. The conductor raised his baton. Dark blue plush curtains parted and there, against a huge mirrored backdrop, stood a slim erect vision of femininity, with exquisite coiffure above an oval face, and long-lashed eyes that were limpid pools of mystery and witchery unparalleled.

She wore an ankle-length, tight sheath of velvet in crushed-raspberry color which accented her flawless complexion, displaying perfect arms and shoulders. A rope of diamonds circled her tiny waist and on her head rested a triumph of the jeweler's art, a tiara of diamonds set in delicate filigree. On her feet were slender high-heeled slippers, suggestive of Cinderella's fabled glass footwear. All this richness of setting was as nothing compared to the authentic, living beauty at its focal point. The audience caught its breath, broke into a spontaneous ripple of applause which subsided as Mara began to sing.

Who could describe that lilting voice, powerful, true and sweet; expressing all the emotion implicit in the aria; a voice not forced, never sacrificing the tender innocent naivete of lovely, pathetic Lucia? Next day, the critics of the press were to exhaust their adjectives in adulation. That night, listeners knew they were witnessing opera history in the making. An awed moment of stillness followed the final double-bar; then, applause was thunderous. She took bow after bow; it was evident that even to gaze upon Mara's fresh glowing young beauty was a thing to dazzle this select group of jaded Parisians, while talent, added to charm, proved an intoxicating draught.

At length Mara signaled to the orchestra leader for an encore, and the audience went completely wild as it realized the next aria would be the *Caro Nome* from *Rigoletto.* "Old war-horses," murmured the woman nearest Achala to her escort, who replied: "Ridden by a real equestrienne."

And now the spirit was entirely changed; pathos was gone; all was exultant joy, unmarred by premonitions. The sympathetic audience followed each successive intonation with greedy rapture; they still could not credit such unheralded artistry from a slim ingenue-type girl.

While the encore was in progress, an usher silently lifted the curtain behind the box where Achala sat entranced. The boy whispered, "Monsieur Achala" and held out a program which was received mechanically. Achala glanced at it hurriedly. On its cover was scribbled in pencil: *Bring scarf immed. to my dress. rm.*

Scarf? Immediately? Dressing room? Yes, the lace trifle lay safe in his pocket. Achala followed the boy backstage, paused in the wings to glimpse the singer's exquisite profile, and to catch the tricky ending of the aria delivered with ease and abandon. He did not reach the dressing room; onstage was far too exciting. Ten times was Mara recalled by an audience gone mad. The eleventh time she appeared wearing a cape of priceless blue mink flung over her deep pink gown, and held up her hand to speak. In the instant hush she told them, enunciating her words clearly in those wonderful caressing tones:

"I thank you, I thank you from the depths of my heart. My orchestra has used up all its scorings, so I shall have to say goodnight, my dear ones, good night." She kissed both hands to them, but they clamored for yet another song. And then Mara did the unprecedented. Had Achala not seen it, he would not have believed it.

There was a small upright piano, closed and standing backstage. Mara motioned to two men to push it forward. Then she gently drew a little, shrinking middle-aged woman from where she stood in the wings weeping with happiness. Mara said:

"The problem is solved, ladies and gentlemen. I will sing once more, and my dear aunt, who has stood by and urged me on, since I was seven years old, to prepare me for this moment — my dear devoted aunt, Mlle. Arifa Hani, will accompany me in the Shadow Song from *Dinorah.*"

At that the roof fell in, figuratively speaking. Aunt Arifa brushed the tears from her eyes, wondered if her dark green silk hung straight, settled herself at the small upright, and played the accompaniment without notes, as she had played it five hundred times for her darling in practice sessions. Mara, knowing that Achala was safely on leash and sharing her triumph, sang like an angel on leave from heaven. Aunt Arifa gave a tremendously good account of herself. At the finish, the audience surged forward onstage, making it impossible to close the curtains, and pandemonium reigned.

Presently, Mara disengaged herself and escaped to the side of Achala, who took possession of her as if she belonged to him and propelled her toward the rear exit. She said: "Darling, I knew you'd come. Wasn't it wonderful? You haven't a date with anyone else, have you?" Achala for once was speechless. She continued: "We must look after Aunt Arifa, though. You don't know about her, do you? She's a frustrated concert pianist. Studied for years, here and in London, before I was born. Made a flop on her debut recital, would never try again. Went back home and made a vocalist out of me. The sudden success tonight — well look, she's twenty years younger already. Who is the old man talking to her?"

The "old man" turned out to be Sir Gerald Ripney of Cobbles Court, in the South of England. Beaming, he held Arifa Hani's hands and proclaimed: "My favorite concert pianist, some twenty years ago. You retired? Ridiculous! Play better than ever, upon my word! Magnificent support, spur of the moment, and all that! Gave your all to this marvelous niece — no wonder she's tops, couldn't be otherwise. I see she has her escort. Now the four of us must go to Maxim's for a bite of something substantial. Don't often find an old friend under such happy circumstances; calls for celebration, don't you know!"

Aunt Arifa, almost fainting with joy, could only nod acquiescence. Mara and Achala pleaded plans of their own; the two couples went their separate ways, Aunt Arifa hardly noticing the presence of Achala, and too drugged with emotion to care.

"I'd like to take you to my apartment," said Mara to Achala, "but my chaperon has walked out on me, and the concierge . . . "

"Let me call a taxicab," interrupted Achala. "We can drive until morning, and begin getting acquainted."

"What a wonderful idea!" she said.

CHAPTER 4

A WARMING FRIENDSHIP

Mara now faced a four-week interval between her highly successful recital in Paris and her opera debut in Milano. She was under contract to rehearse with the cast during the last week prior to the *Lucia* presentation at La Scala. Ordinarily she would have been ultra-keyed up by all the thousand details of costuming, polishing the stage business, keeping her voice in trim, consulting her agent as to press releases, getting enough rest and sleep, re-examining the mechanics of her dramatic interpretation, and so on indefinitely.

But something had happened. It was true that she had worshipped Achala, from a distance, nearly all her life. Her own docile disposition, and the pressure of her family to preserve their fixed social status, to be loyal to their clan, and to develop her artistic talent through rigid application with no letdown, year after year, had insulated her from romance. At the same time, continual listening to, and looking at, operatic performances, plus subjecting herself to sharing those most devastating of emotional outbursts without, however, experiencing emotional reality for herself, had repressed her natural transition from adolescence to early womanhood, until the moment of self-emancipation had arrived explosively. It was well for Mara that the one who prompted her blossoming into sudden maturity was a man of highest ideals and complete understanding. He had, through many torturous weeks, envisioned her as being just what she miraculously was — a beautiful, gifted, many-sided unspoiled example of perfect young womanhood. Each was struck as by lightning with the advent of such a heaven-sent partner. Each went about the daily routine with ecstasy in every thought, in every action.

It is worthy of note that each *did* adhere to fixed responsibilities; neither thought of dodging or postponing them.

Both Mara and Achala felt their sensibilities and capabilities infinitely enhanced. As their thoughts and ambitions merged, it was as if some mighty force had removed all finite limits to attainment, everything seemed easy. She sang like a theater impresario's dream. He analyzed and expanded his Plan for their beloved homeland's future security and peace.

Letters from home were discouraging and gave Achala no indication that it would be practical for him to return.

Little by little Achala explained to Mara his present mission in life. She listened raptly, intelligently. Soon he felt he had her complete sympathy and confidence. But still he asked, frankly:

"Dearest Mara, do my views conflict basically or in any way at all with your feelings and convictions? You know that your kinsmen and mine do not fully agree."

"I know that, Achala, my dear, dear friend. I see very clearly that your dream for our country's freedom is at variance with the thoughts and practices of my father, my brothers, my uncles, and my cousins. At the same time, I am Mara, an individual, a Patriot, and am blessed with a mind of my own which I have had unusual opportunity to develop. I have some personal opinions of what is right and just, and I have had to use a little executive ability in shaping my own career, or what promises to be a career. Aunt Arifa hasn't done it all, you know."

Achala smiled. "I had deduced that. But I love the way you build up her ego in public. By the way, what's become of Aunt Arifa? We don't see much of her. I had the impression she would be constantly on hand and urging you to practice for La Scala."

Mara could not restrain a mischievous little laugh. She said: "You mean, you haven't seen her bubbling around, bothering us. Well, there are three good reasons for that. Want to know what they are?"

"Can't wait," he said adoringly.

"First," she said, checking them off on her fingers, "I assured my dear aunt, in no uncertain terms, that, if she interferes with my artistic temperament and its expression with so much as one tiny little objection to anything, during these next weeks, I will personally cancel my appearance in *Lucia* and let La Scala refund all the money for tickets on a sold-out house. Aunt Arifa knew I meant what I said. It would wreck her to have that happen."

"Bravo!" said Achala in high amusement. "What next, my diva?"

"Second — she is perfectly aware that I know the role of Lucia, I can sing and act it in my sleep; for she herself has done much of the coaching and I can tell you it was thorough. Besides, last spring I sang it in an unpublicized command performance for the Queen of the Netherlands and her daughters; so I know that I am letter-perfect in the part. I am vocalizing each day and doing all my health exercises, and shall have one week of rehearsal in Italy to acquaint me with any local variations in the presentation."

"Bueno!" exclaimed Achala gleefully. "I had wondered about it, why you didn't seem nervous or worried."

"Oh, preparation means everything. Some singers cultivate stage fright, say it helps them to give a better performance, but I think not. Number Three is confidential—do you want to hear it?"

"Do I?" said Achala eagerly, knowing from the merriment in her eyes that this reason might be the most interesting of all.

"Very well, but it's a deep dark secret, so far. You remember Sir Gerald Ripney, of Cobbles Court, in England?"

"Oh yes, he's the old duck who appeared so opportunely at the palace and diverted Aunt Arifa's attention from us. I only wish he had been on the boat that night."

"But this is better yet," she insisted. "He told her she played magnificently, you know. Well, she really did outdo herself, in all the excitement and surprise. Now Sir Gerald, a genteel widower for many years, who has several children back at Cobbles Court, is squiring Aunt Arifa around Paris—he knows all the right people; and she, poor dear, is getting younger by the minute, and neglecting me in fine fashion. I can't figure out yet whether he means to marry her, or to engage her as governess for his children. For her sake, I hope it's the former, though I can testify that she would shine in the latter role."

Both laughed heartily. Achala said, with wonder in his tone: "We even enjoy the same jokes, don't we? Of course, Aunt Arifa is not exactly a joke."

"Oh, but if you only knew the way she has put me through my paces, since I was seven years old, Achala; if you knew how she has frowned on any splinter of romance, you *would* see the joke. Now tell me more about the work you're doing to free Alpaca from dictatorship. That is far more important than anything I have ever tried to accomplish."

He said thoughtfully: "I know of Sir Gerald's position and influence in England. If he is going to get our permission to woo Aunt Arifa, he must share with us his knowledge and his contacts."

He looked at her with yearning but with utter directness.

"Mara, do not deceive me, do not trifle with me. You have my devotion, but I must tell you that I love my country more. So tell me the truth. Can you go on with me, truly and uncompromisingly, even though your people should disapprove?"

She placed both her hands in his, looked into his eyes with candor.

"Achala," she said quietly, "I too love my country more than life itself, more than I could love any individual. If my people are in the wrong, I may be able gradually to

win them over. Ah, you shake your head. Then leave that
in the realm of the unknown, the unknowable. I will try,
for I think that they are now shortsighted. I may fail. In
either event, my Achala, my heart is yours and my loyalty
is yours, if decisive choice must be made. I know from
what you've told me, that you and your group are self-
lessly dedicated to our country's good. You may depend
on me . . . darling."

He held her close, and murmured: "We were made for
each other. It was foreordained that we should be united.
You know that, don't you?"

For answer, she turned to him with faith in her eyes.
Each felt happiness touching the sublime. Presently he put
his plea into words:

"Will you help me further this plan for just government?
Will you do me the honor of working with me and the
friends I have made?"

"Yes, Achala," Mara promised, and he could not doubt
her. "Tell me as much, or as little, as you please. I am
with you, all the way!"

So it came about that Mara was enlisted in the cause;
now there were two where there had been one, crusading
for a better, fairer, safer Alpaca.

Soon it became apparent that Achala had recruited an
exceptional ally. They made a forceful team—each complemented the other. Each recognized the other as an individual. He would have urged immediate marriage, but with
her pending debut—the culmination of a lifetime of ar-
duous labor—they knew they must wait a while. It would
not be fair to ask her for so great an adjustment, at this
particular moment.

When together they got down to real study, Mara began
to learn from Achala more about the enthusiasts he had
gathered about him since he had been in Europe and their

differing ideas for building government ideally suited to a small country.

She asked, "Where did you get your drive to devise a political plan for curing existing evils?"

Achala thoughtfully replied, "Our eldest and wisest have been debating among themselves for years, just what steps to take. Keenly aware of their limitations and lack of practical experience, they knew that their accumulated knowledge came down largely from the distant past."

Seeing her interest, Achala went on: "Orlando Tasso, the great Italian lawyer, examined what we had done and gave us further impetus. We read Aristotle and other ancient thinkers who discussed government. But there is little parallel between the present and the ancient world where the slaves outnumbered free men sometimes in a ratio of four to one. Alpaca, of course, is a country of free and equal citizens—theoretically so, at any rate; it goes without saying that dictatorship will eventually divide the people of any land into a slave class and an elite."

"And that is why it must be headed off," said Mara, nodding in a practical way.

"Yes, positively, before it is too late. In a free country, the impulse of public policy must come from below, through layers of education. Despite a debasing slave system which perhaps led to their state's ultimate undoing, the more intelligent of the ancient Greeks were, beyond question, stumbling toward our own idea that rule should be in the hands of the responsible and the Patriotic."

"I mean to learn your Plan by heart, so that I can talk, think and plan with you. I'll study it, I promise you—I'll steep myself in it, from now until I go to Milano and after I come back to Paris—as if it were a new operatic role I had made up my mind to learn. I know fourteen roles already, a great number for a novice, and Alpaca's Plan shall be my fifteenth."

Achala looked at her with worship in his eyes. Their natures were so different, yet they complemented each other so well. "I love you, Mara," he said simply.

"That's what I want most," she said softly, "more than my own career. But not more than the welfare of our country. We're together on that. The point is, I believe in your Plan, even before I take it on for my fifteenth role, because, Achala, I believe in you."

"Thank you, Mara," he said humbly.

"Even though I'm trained to be a singing artist," she explained, "I've gone about my studies in a businesslike way. Every little thing was planned for that recital you heard, even the rumors about the mysterious newcomer." She looked roguish for an instant. "You and your friends have worked out the right solution for Alpaca, I'm sure of that: that's your specialty, not mine. But I can help you sell it to the people, Achala." Her tone was very serious. "I can help you put it over, my darling. As soon as I can get this debut out of the way, we'll make a Team. Oh, what a Team! We'll perfect the details here, then go back home and show the people what's good for them. What do you say?"

"It sounds . . . as beautiful as your singing, Mara. How can I say more?"

"How long will it take," she asked practically, "to get your Plan in finished form?"

"Oh, I don't know, I can't tell . . ."

"But how much longer?" she insisted. "Time is a factor, in anything."

He remembered that Tasso too had warned, "Time is a factor."

"Yes, and especially now, with government almost everywhere either in too fluid form or tending to become fixed, rigid, outside the people's power." Achala paused, concentrating on the time factor which was, he knew, vastly important. "I have considerably more to do here. I was supposed to visit The Hague, Cairo, and Jerusalem, though if conditions at home look threatening I could skip those places. London was on my itinerary before Paris, but I shifted."

He smiled and blushed, which made Mara love him all the more. "I really ought to go to London for a fortnight. That possibly would get the purely theoretical work under control, or place it at least in the domain of future correspondence."

"Darling, a little thought comes to me," said Mara. "You were thinking of flying to Milano for *Lucia,* were you not?"

"Don't put it in the past tense," he said reproachfully. "I intend to be there. Don't you want me?"

"Oh, now I have hurt you," Mara exclaimed, "and I did not mean to do that. Of course I want you there, my Achala. Your presence would inspire me, as it did when I saw you in that box at the palace. But I shall be intensively occupied for a solid week; we would be able to see very little of each other. It seems to me that your work is too urgent and important to be interrupted and you should go to London on schedule."

Achala said helplessly: "I am putty in your hands—direct me, my diva."

CHAPTER 5

PROVISIONS OF CONSTITUTION

Achala made arrangements to go to London for one week, as Mara had suggested. The days remaining until they would be separated seemed to him the most precious of his life. They were days filled with study and discussion among individuals and groups of students whom he had come to know, and Mara was sometimes present. The first time she joined them, Achala presented her with pride. She fitted easily into the group. She was devoting the mornings to her professional routine but keeping afternoons free, even with her great ordeal fast approaching.

"It is not really an ordeal to you, is it?" he said one day when they were alone, "singing the role of Lucia, I mean."

"I am well drilled in it, Achala," she replied calmly, "I am keeping myself in condition. I am happy because I have you. Why should anything be an ordeal? Not long ago I might have been less poised. Something has happened to me. Opera has been my ambition all these years. I looked forward to the time when I should give pleasure to audiences and compel admiration. Since I have known you all that seems less important. Your patient explanations have made me see how vital good government is. I only want to get this debut over, because I owe it to my friends and to my former ideals and ambitions. When I have proved myself a success, I shall come back to you and help you save our country from those trying to ruin it—whoever they are," she added with meaning.

"Mara, Mara, you are superb. You never fear failure, do you?"

"What is failure? It is lack of preparation. I shall be tense before I go on the stage that night, but I shall not be afraid. A few hours of tenseness—what of that?"

"You are so brave," said Achala. "Most of us would

tremble to meet so great a challenge. Your idea of full and detailed preparation is like mine, in the drafting of our Plan."

"Let us get back to the Plan," she said. "I have not yet made it my fifteenth role, but I am studying it and find it fascinating."

"Truly, do you, Mara?" he asked, for he had feared she might find it technical, hence forbidding. Above all, he hoped the concerted effort of so many dedicated workers would produce a worthy document which the man in the street, the worker in the vineyard, the housewife rocking the cradle, the shepherd at his lonely outpost, and the soldier in his barracks, could understand.

"I don't see how you could have made it clearer," she told him; and no music from her lips ever sounded sweeter to his ear. "I want you to go on from where we left off yesterday, and impart to me a fraction of your wisdom."

This, coming from Mara, was a request not to be denied.

Notwithstanding Mara's approaching debut at La Scala, Milano and, vastly more important, their intended marriage, Achala and Mara took great pride in the highly intelligent group of friends who were becoming interested with them in the Plan.

Naturally they received great diversity of opinion from their many counselors. In their visits and studies they did not confine themselves to any one class, age, profession, nationality or station in life. Both became astute investigators, historians and researchers in the social science, trying to incorporate everything they learned in a Plan wherein peace and freedom would be uppermost.

When they sensed danger in being over-influenced by information they were receiving from any particular source, one or the other of them would promptly see the opposite point of view from contrary sources and get information to offset that which they were about to accept before they were sufficiently informed. They repeatedly reviewed any phase of government about which they felt they had been reaching a hasty conclusion.

It seemed that nearly all members of the Team understood that they must not talk each other into impotence while trying to get something done.

Mara and Achala were ever indebted to those who advanced the decisive thinking and reasoning which resulted in the use of any section or clause in the Plan. Many Team members earned commendation in connection with their proposal for a draft of a part of the Plan. In discussing these good friends, one day Mara injected a question, "What about the ones who have offered ideas which we did not finally accept?" After a lengthy talk they decided they were equally indebted to those Team members whose contributions were never accepted. It was they who furnished the background which made Mara and Achala all the more sure of the provisions upon which they decided. They were the constructive critics of whom we so often hear; the staunch opposition is another way of saying it. They offered the basis for comparison from which the best was selected with a firm conviction that it was the best.

For example, there was Josef Holbrecht, the 22-year-old from Salzburg, Austria, who possessed an IQ beyond compare with that of any other brain-truster on the Team. He had the rare combination of force along with thoughtfulness. It was nearly impossible to dismiss some of his views even when they varied from the best that were advanced from any other source. There was considerable merit in all views expressed so ably by Josef, yet in nearly all cases his thinking was ultimately rejected. Often it was for technical reasons, such as the impossibility of administration. Many of Josef's views failed to be incorporated on the theory that, in a government based on fairness and justice, what is good for the possessor of the greatest wealth in the Nation is good for the poorest citizen or the citizen in any degree of prosperity between these extremes.

Frequently someone referred to the USA as the "Model Republic." A happy addition to the Plan Team family were the likeable Americanos, Robert and Betty Brown from Abilene, Kansas, one of the towns claiming "Ike" for its own. Bob and Betty's background was interesting to all because they had dealt with life in its actuality rather than theory. Betty had been a secretary in a large department store in Chicago, and Bob an industrial worker in Detroit. During a visit Bob made to Chicago, they met and after a short romance, were married. Both of them were farm reared and had an innate love of the land. They pooled their savings, purchased a farm near Abilene, becoming their own bosses in a modest farming operation in that grain and livestock region. At the end of three years they had succeeded far beyond their expectations and to the extent that they decided a delayed honeymoon was in order. Such sweet success often rewards the individual who is master of his destiny.

In Roma they had met and liked Juan Achala. He had so many questions to ask about life in the USA, as they had seen and lived it, that they excitedly searched their memories for all the information they could possibly convey to this likeable young man, to help him with his Plan. Wherever he was, the Browns kept contact with him, and at his suggestion would visit and compare notes with others of Achala's new-found friends in whatever country they happened to be.

In their discussions with other members of the Plan Team, Bob and Betty Brown injected a thought-provoking question: if a republic is established, how long will it last? Drawing from the experience of their own country, the Browns emphasized the fact that once a republic is established it will come to have divisive internal elements seeking to tear it down. This is inevitable, they advised, because the freedom of a republic rightfully allows dissent, up to the point of anarchy or sedition. The Browns stressed that the Plan Team should keep this in mind in drafting the Constitution for Alpaca, and should pattern this document to eliminate loop-holes for those who would seek to destroy it. Bob and Betty also related, from their own firsthand experience, the fact that when a republic is so threatened, it will be saved — if it is saved—only by people whose political persuasion is to the Right of average. The logic of this conclusion was based on the fact that middle-of-the-roaders — the "moderates," the neutrals—will not stand up in defense of the republic. Indeed, some of the "moderates" succumb to the pressures exerted by the collectivists who historically undermine republics, and the "moderates" resist only to the extent of urging "moderation" or gradualism, the Browns said. The young couple frequently cited the fact that even a large segment of businessmen in their country abstained from showing any more than token signs of patriotism, because they had been sold a "line" for thirty years: that it was "bad for business" to do so, that it would alienate labor, disturb stockholders, lose customers, and so forth—which is far from the truth, the Browns hastened to add.

Achala had believed that romance was, for him, a thing to be repressed and postponed until the great work upon which he was embarked should be finished. One thing at a time, he told himself sternly. But Mara's luscious personality was a force he had not reckoned with. Her intense interest in his cause drew them more closely together, and within a shorter time than any match-making diviner of tea leaves or clairvoyant could have predicted. As Achala reluctantly took a plane for London, he realized anew how his life had become keyed to a subtle undercurrent of change. That the week ahead would, however, prove fruitful he felt certain. Aunt Arifa had mentioned to Sir Gerald Ripney that Achala was about to cross the Channel in quest of further knowledge, whereupon that genial gentleman came forward with time-saving lists of persons in government who could be depended upon to provide information and stimulating ideas.

"Great mission you're on, young man," he said. "Begin with Magna Charta, trace the rise of good government down to present-day British Commonwealth, best of all possible systems. Would be happy to take you around London myself, but the girls have graciously consented to let me go along to Milano, carry packages, open doors for them, that sort of thing. Wouldn't miss *Lucia,* Scottish idyll and all that, don't you know. Will bring back full report." His ruddy face beamed with delight.

Contacts in and near London contributed to Achala's search for practical information and guidance. His goal, obviously, was to construct a workable Plan for a faraway land whose people had never known benign laws. This appealed to several Britishers of high mentality and vivid imagination who could appreciate the daring of such an effort. The English enjoy protection, gradually evolved, against injustice, without formality of a written constitution. They forthwith became staunch friends and supporters of Achala's project, promising continued research and correspondence.

It was heartening to have strangers cease being strangers, taking the Plan seriously. Despite the Plan Team's deep-seated resolve never to let their dream-government degenerate into monarchy, Achala would carry through life a warm, cozy feeling of regard for the British Isles and their inhabitants, with their gentle words of veneration for Royalty.

And then he was again on a plane, Paris-bound, at almost

the very hour of Mara's debut. He longed to fly to her side, but prudence restrained him. His backers at home would consider such a detour beyond the wise expenditure of time and money and, besides, Mara had advised against it. He could appreciate the fact that she must withdraw from his orbit and, by supreme act of will, concentrate on this crowning episode in her own career. Moment by moment, Achala envisioned her as she lived through possible mishaps and miscues. Would she prove her mettle and vindicate her faith in preparedness, as a shield and buckler against those demons of nervousness which, Achala had long understood, beset the seasoned prima donna as well as the untried beginner?

He need have had no qualms. Awaiting Achala in his hotel lobby was Sir Gerald Ripney, just in by plane from Milano, laden with newspapers carrying the reviews, aglow with more than usual enthusiasm. He exclaimed:

"Tremendous audience response and ovation! Not so much as one slip in the entire performance! Mara was beautiful, beautiful! Never saw such poise. From now on, she has the world of music at her feet. And to think, the future Lady Ripney devoted so much of her life to training this lovely star! Congratulate me, my boy, on my good fortune."

Even prior to the Ripney nuptials, Mara and Achala were united in a simple civil ceremony in Paris, where a few of their new friends gathered, gay and joyous, inclined to throw rice and old shoes. The event was devoid of pomp and show which would have attended it, had this union of the Achala and Hani families taken place in Alpaca. The press could not be kept away, most reporters regarding the marriage as a fitting climax to the bride's recent triumph.

The two principals felt their union gave added impetus to the great objective of bringing freedom to Alpaca.

Although their country's destiny had become the paramount influence in their lives, and they were dedicated to the principles of Liberty, Justice, and Peace, there had to be a short interval for them to pursue what might be called a policy of isolationism. One precious week of "getting-to-know-you" they allowed themselves in a heavenly retreat on the Riviera.

That first night they stood awhile on a balcony overlooking the starlit Mediterranean, in ecstasy—almost speechless —but not quite. Yielding to the protective curve of his arm, Mara whispered:

"No more trumped-up love scenes with a screeching tenor."

"No more stage kisses," Achala assured her.

"No more fake emotions," she gloated.

"Or artificial leers," he said firmly. "The real thing, or nothing."

She shivered a little, in pure bliss. He whipped a frothy lace trifle from his pocket.

"Ah," she breathed reproachfully, "You never returned my property."

"Just because," he explained, "at the time I received it, I vowed a vow to replace it on the shoulders of my lawful wedded wife."

Enraptured, they let conversation languish, while waves lapped gently against the beach below, and the incurious moon rose slowly.

CHAPTER 6

THE PLAN TEAM

The small coterie enthusiastically working with Achala and Mara on the Plan came to be spoken of as "The Group," "The Team" or "Plan Team." Soon they and their friends laughingly spoke of "The Triumvirate—Achala, Mara, Alpaca."

From the start, there was realization by all in the Group that, in any revision of government, the most important element would be the citizens of the country. As the thinking was uniform on a government framed in Lincoln's immortal words, "of the people, by the people," they could all agree readily that the proposed Constitution would create a representative government elected through democracy. But beyond this, opinion proved diverse. Who are "the people" in the voting sense? In electing officials, should the criterion at the polls be "one man, one vote?" Or should there be recognition, in providing voting qualifications, that people do differ? It was pointed out that some citizens are better qualified by superior education or attainments to exercise judgment than are others. Again for various reasons some make greater contributions to general good than others. If these conditions are admitted, should better-qualified or more-devoted citizens have greater voting power than the mill run of people? There was no unanimity in thinking on this problem. There were arguments from various angles and for differing proposals in the Group. All realized that the proper provision for national suffrage was the fundamental requirement for the Constitution. But there was so much argument pro and con on the suggestions advanced that no agreement could be reached on an over-all accepted solution.

This was not true, of course, of all ideas on suffrage that were presented. There was little disagreement in the Group on the general idea of universal suffrage for all classes and ages beyond maturity. Few voices were raised against votes for women. But on some other plans, it was evident that a great deal of further study and exploration of historic experience would be necessary. So it was agreed on Achala's suggestion that other aspects of the Constitution would be taken up and decided, that suffrage would be further discussed from time to time as reports were made and ideas advanced. This procedure was followed with the result that the Group agreement on suffrage remained open until many of the last phases of the Constitution were achieved.

Initially, the thinking centered on allowing one vote to younger qualified registrants, increasing this to two votes at the more mature age of 22. But it was pointed out that this proposal impaired the basic idea of uniform suffrage. The idea of selective suffrage was presented during the argument, but either diplomatically or ruthlessly was avoided, discredited, refuted, or rejected. While it made no headway with the Team, one inquisitive member kept the subject alive by asking some questions apparently for his own information or perhaps satisfaction.

Jan Wauskoski posed his question in a summarizing statement to the group, but the question and the summary were both intended to elicit a response from Holbrecht. "Some of us," Jan began, "are thinking about woman's suffrage when we talk of universal suffrage. Or we confuse universal suffrage with uniform suffrage. I believe that what we've been talking about, up to now, is uniform suffrage; and what we need, at this point, is a common ground of understanding. Just what is uniform suffrage? If a decision can be made as to what uniform suffrage is, we will know a great deal more about what we are trying to settle. I believe our group will be divided as to the minimum age for suffrage, but we could probably agree on some age from 18 through 21 years. There must be a requirement for a length of residence in Alpaca or in the voter's province of residence, I would think.

"Unquestionably, there must be a form of registration for prospective voters, and a voter should be properly registered before being allowed to vote in any election.

"But we could talk at length, and get into some fine arguments, about any of these points, without knowing if we are talking about the same things. So I would like to see a written draft which would establish uniform suffrage for Alpaca. If such a draft can be agreed upon, basically, then we would all have a common point of reference should anyone in the future propose to depart from the provisions of uniform suffrage."

Achala nodded his approval of Jan's observation, and Holbrecht, as Jan expected, volunteered: "I shall work toward preparing a very concise draft of the qualifications for voting in Alpaca."

Holbrecht started his draft by defining the difference between universal suffrage and uniform suffrage. For the purposes of this draft, he stated, universal suffrage was considered "the extension of the vote to all persons above a given age, with no further qualifications." Uniform suffrage, he wrote, was "the application of uniform qualifications for voting, to all persons given the right to vote by the Constitution." Holbrecht then stated that uniform suffrage was the system to be instituted by the draft of the Group position.

In the draft, Holbrecht restrained himself from editorializing for his own points of view. He limited the draft to basic considerations, leaving some controversial points for resolution by the Group, and expecting that some additional qualifications — including his own ideas, if he could sell them to the Group — would be added before the draft would be incorporated into a final Group position paper for inclusion in the Constitution.

The draft called for the vote to be extended to all persons except felons, 18 years of age and above, regardless of sex, race, creed, or color. It specified that each citizen of Alpaca, native or naturalized, would be qualified to vote in all national elections, and that qualification for voting in provincial elections would depend upon residence in a precinct of the province for not less than three months. Voter registration was specified in the draft by a requirement for each voter to register each year, in his local precinct, and obtain a registration certificate qualifying him to vote in all elections to be held during that year by any level of government.

After Holbrecht presented his draft of qualifications for uniform suffrage to the Group, there was no lack of discussion. Debate continued, but now it was based on the common ground of the draft's proposals. And other points, as Jan had expected, were revived and discussed in the light of the draft as an aftermath to the preparation of the draft, which kept the members of the team on common ground with which many were familiar.

Meanwhile, the Group proceeded to bring up, examine, debate and decide other issues. Achala, mindful that the future of any country lies in its young people, wanted to introduce the youth of Alpaca to the responsibility of citizenship and encourage them to share in government at a much younger age than is usually allowed. After all, he pointed out, many fundamental ideas in science and other fields were first formulated in the minds of persons under twenty years of age.

Members of the Team applauded the principle of channeling the boundless energy and laudable verve of youth into constructive endeavors. They recognized that youth is a time for causes, and too often if young people are left on their own they will search out causes of doubtful value to champion.

Josef thought that citizens between 18 and 21 years of age might be given half the voting power of other voters as an offset to inexperience and possible poor judgment. Other Team members objected, however, that this plan would be an infringement on the principle of uniform suffrage.

In objecting to age being permitted to destroy uniformity of suffrage, Sir Gerald stated that "Susan B. Anthony with her votes for women had badly undermined the sacred right of suffrage and voting power of men who, after all, were responsible for the conduct of government free from irrational sentimentality."

In discussing the brave step of uniform suffrage, several of those consulted urged that, while of course mental cases would be denied the vote, sanity and educational tests should be imposed as qualifications for voting, but this proposal was rejected by others in whom Achala had the utmost confidence. In the end, the Plan Team decided against either an educational or a sanity test. They decided that the citizen's contribution to the government makes him a much more desirable voter than any grading which might be given him for what he is supposed to know.

Educational tests were taboo because they could be too easily manipulated by election officials to disfranchise some voters, and the tests could never be made uniform. It seemed to the Team that many of the bad political decisions which have blackened human history have been made by the so-called "educated," whose minds have been warped and twisted by bookish theories which have no relationship to political reality. The Team early agreed that nowhere else can such abysmal ignorance be found as is displayed among the most highly educated.

On the other hand, many men and women with little formal schooling have shown a high degree of statesmanship. Betty Brown, prideful of their sex, told Mara of a wife who had taught her husband, who later became an able President of the USA, to read and write. They were also moved by the story of King Ibn Saud who could neither read nor write. Despite this fact, and against great odds, he succeeded in welding the flimsy warring tribes of a large part of Arabia into the fairly workable National entity of Saudi Arabia. Ibn Saud was said to have known literally hundreds of thousands of Arabs by name. Yet, under an educational test, he would have been deprived of a vote.

The Team also decided a lunacy test unnecessary and indeed wrong. In the first place, very few lunatics would attempt to vote. Mental patients who did would probably vote as sensibly as the average in suffrage countries have been voting in recent years. Any attempt by election officials to determine the sanity of voters would be cumbersome, a sure source of harmful publicity, and could create untold injustice.

Upholding the contrary, Josef Holbrecht declared there was an absolute necessity for a sanity test. He contended that without this test the confidence of the electorate would be destroyed in that they could feel that their individual vote might be offset by the vote of a lunatic.

The Team heard and granted there was some merit to his contention, but further found that less than 10 per cent of the voters were mental cases; probably as few as one in 3 would ever go to the polls and, if they did, they would not represent a bloc vote but would vote as individuals, and in a runoff could be expected to vote about 50 per cent for each of two candidates. There would be probably as few as one in twenty from what some would consider a normal sanity.

This mental case vote might represent the balance in power in as few as *one in a thousand elections*. To further consider their competency in voting, it is well known that persons affected mentally are not necessarily unwise because with their aberration they develop a sixth sense which gives them an insight beyond that of the normal person who has the usual five senses of perception.

Sir Gerald Ripney here inserted a touch of British humor that drew a laugh from the Team and helped defeat the Holbrecht argument. He said that Josef should have included the uneducated and the insane in his selective suffrage plan by giving the unlucky in these categories one vote, other citizens two, which would serve his purpose as well as elimination.

The machinery for the Registration Board to judge who is and who is not sane enough to vote would be cumbersome, slow, expensive, and the test or trial would result in needless adverse publicity to the unfortunate having mental trouble, and could result in long-lasting and great harm. The exercise of this test could bring the Judiciary into disrepute and, for Registrars and others, could result in a serious cause of action for denying a person the right to vote.

With important provisions of the Plan beginning to get wrapped up, Achala, happy with the progress which had been made, realized that construction, development, and industrialization were in the offing for Alpaca. This would become a new and unknown factor with which a new government in Alpaca would soon be required to deal. The relative rights of the investor, management and labor must be anticipated and placed in position where they could be adjudged.

Few on the Plan Team, except Bob and Betty Brown, could be expected to come up with reliable information and helpful ideas regarding labor. Through Sir Gerald, Achala learned of the intensive study made by Jim Welsh, a canny young Scot, grandson of a noted labor leader famous in the annals of labor history. Achala contacted Welsh and found him to be a clear, revolutionary thinker who believed that if the laboring man were protected from the hardships and indignities which could be often heaped upon him, the attitude of Labor would never become one which would menace government, upset the economy and work a hardship on the general public. Welsh and Achala agreed that, if the problems of labor could be anticipated and solved in advance, all other factors could easily adjust to their proper function.

CHAPTER 7

DELEGATE SYSTEM AND VACANCIES

Gradually, as he assembled his facts and the shape of the needed Plan took form in his mind, Achala concluded that the Constitution must be one peculiarly fitted to a small, compact country like Alpaca with its kind, simple people and its predominantly agricultural economy. Manifestly it might not apply to a larger and more diversified national life. Having thus delineated his subject, Achala decided that the answer to "The Man" in Alpaca was a Constitution which would make dictatorship impossible and extinct. This could be accomplished, he reasoned, if the form of government assigned to every citizen a reasonable part and function in the governing process. Where everyone participates, none can monopolize authority.

As Sir Gerald pointed out, in nations dominated by a state religion, the amount of the citizen's contribution to the Church decides his power. In Alpaca, the deciding factor would be his contribution to the government.

For purposes of voting and representation, all Alpaca is divided into precincts,[1] each containing approximately 2,000 voters, with a vastly superior system for elections to any in use anywhere outside Alpaca, functioning as follows:

The voters of the precinct elect a Registration Board of three, for terms of twelve (12) years, one board member being elected every four years. The Board maintains a registration office where every citizen is required to register at the mutual convenience of the citizens and registrars within a prescribed time. Voting is not compulsory, but registration is.[2]

The Precinct Registration Boards, six months before the quadrennial elections, begin to accept nominations from any

[1]*Art. I, Sec. 2*
[2]*Art. I, Sec. 3*

individual citizen for nominations to the delegateships to which the precinct is entitled, in the four respective categories: Executive, Legislative, Judicial and Military.[3] One-third of the total number of delegates are elected every four years. The Board prepares the ballots on which appear the names of citizens receiving the requisite number of nomination proposals. Two elections are held—a first election, in which all names qualified by petition appear; and a run-off election two (2) weeks later, at which final choice is made between the two (2) receiving the highest vote in each category. Half of the delegates elected in all except the Military branch, are designated as Place 1 delegates, to fill local or regional offices. The other half, as Place 2 delegates, become members of the college of delegates from this and other nearby precincts, up to the number of 300.[4]

Delegates from a precinct are chosen to become a part of and form a college of 300 or fewer delegates from nearby precincts. This is the beginning of a pyramidal system of colleges of delegates. The first college will elect delegates, half of whom will be Place 1 delegates to fill the unfilled offices within the area which the college represents and elect the other half as Place 2 delegates to proceed upward in the pyramidal system until the highest college has been formed. The highest college in each branch of government shall elect the highest officers in the land.

The number of delegates in the highest college shall not be confined to 300 and fewer delegates, as in the lower colleges but may contain a maximum of 400 and a minimum of 101 delegates. This departure in number in the highest college from the usual number of delegates in the lower college, is necessary to meet the changes which will take place in population numbers. Otherwise the delegates in the high-

---

[3]*Art. I, Sec. 4*
[4]*Art. I, Sec. 5*

est college might be so few in number that they would not
be considered a proper body to carry out the all-important
duty of choosing the highest officers in the land.

The elections in the first college would be held one month
after the precinct elections and this lapse of time would be
carried out in sequence throughout the elections in the
pyramidal system of colleges.

The voting in precincts may be by closed ballot or voting
machine, but all voting in the colleges of delegates shall be
of record disclosing the vote of each delegate. A delegate in
one branch may serve in the same branch of government in
as many delegate positions as he is elected to hold.

This system of delegation of voting power to keep those
who vote in position to vote within their reasonable acquaintance is a vastly superior system for elections to any
in use anywhere outside Alpaca. In order to retain equality
at all times, each delegate casts the vote of the combined
registered voting power of the area he represents.[5]

Citizens who attained positions high or low were not required to have been the greatest loud promisers, exhorters,
orators, tireless campaigners or thick-skinned survivors of
smear campaigns.

Members of their families could carry on as though there
had been no campaign, instead of furtively picking their way
about with heads hung in shame. Should they have been the
most glib and adroit, this quality availed them not, for the
sweet somethings for nothing they could have promised are
still intact, on hand and remain part of the wonderful heritage
of the land they love.

They were not called upon to promise away the best assets
of their home land to make a successful campaign, for they
had been elected by those who personally knew them or

---

[5]*Art. I, Sec. 4*

have friends who knew them, in a tranquil weighing of the best against the second best and not in a stampede of hysteria. There is nothing to keep them from being reliable Patriots whom their fellow men have hired to serve them and to whom they have pledged their faithful service.

There was more than one reason why rank and file voters were willing to delegate their voting power to another. Many of them decided that they could find someone better informed than they in the Executive branch, someone in the Legislative branch, someone in the Judicial branch, and someone in the Military branch. The voter was acquainted with persons who had often given a large part of their lives to study of the branch of government to which they were devoted.

Bob Brown recalled spending several hours in getting to the polling place and waiting in line to vote. Conscientiously he discovered in dismay that he had convictions sufficient for him to exercise a choice in only three of forty-two offices to be filled in the election. He made up his mind that he would know more about what he was doing the next time he went to vote. He reasoned that it would be much easier for him and many others to delegate their voting power to someone whom they knew had taken time to better qualify himself as to the merit of the candidates.

Bob and Betty contributed this choice morsel. Newsweek Magazine, August 18, 1958, published the story of its representative in Bob's home town, Detroit, on the eve of the primary there, asking 14 voters did they think that William Jennings Bryan would win the next day. William Jennings Bryan had been dead about 33 years. He, the Great Commoner, had been three times a major party's candidate for President of the USA. Seven of the fourteen questioned thought he would win, but were a little uncertain as to the office for which he was running. Betty thought this story laughable, while Bob was inclined to be solemn about it, and their listeners in Europe were frankly shocked.

This was a conclusive argument in favor of the voter's delegating his voting power to a person within his circle of acquaintance, who in turn would exercise the delegated power with specific knowledge.

The Plan for Alpaca provided that each branch of Government would elect a Vacancy Committee to serve only their branch of government. The wisdom of the Vacancy Committee was easily sold to Achala and Mara. Antonio was one of the strongest advocates of this provision. When a vacancy occurs, it is the cessation in office of someone chosen by the Alpacan people, for the branch of government in which it occurs, through its elective processes, even if the vacancy is in an office which has been filled by appointment. It is then fitting and proper that the vacancy for the vacancy period, and that is until the next election, should be filled by Committeemen chosen for that particular purpose. In the Vacancy Committee is reposed the confidence of the electorate of Alpaca, and this wise arrangement can probably be found nowhere else in the world.[6]

Vacancies following death or from any other causes, without regard to the branch of Government in which they have occurred, have been filled by appointment by someone of the Executive Department, often by the head. The choice of an appointee to fill a vacancy has been subject to many considerations entirely unrelated to the capabilities of the appointee. Often the appointment to fill a vacancy was tendered to a friend, often as an honorary gesture, more often with a view of the effect the appointment would have on some race in the next general election.

These were among the matters that received the close attention of Achala and his fellow-workers. The Plan Team

[6]*Art. I, Sec. 7*

had grown to goodly proportions, composed of persons from different walks of life. The Team functioned in a unique way, partly because of the diversity of residence and nationality, with no attempt made to convene the Team for group discussions in which so very little is accomplished considering the amount of brainpower involved.

It was the early conception in the Alpaca Plan that dissemination of information and opinion should be largely confined to the printed word, or word of mouth between two, or at most a few, individuals. In this way, the Plan Team functioned. Any one of them who felt he or she had anything worth while to report to Achala or Mara willingly accepted the thesis that if they knew their subject they could write it in concise form. They were happy to reach headquarters or other members of the team with whom they were acquainted with letters or copies of letters which constituted their thinking on a given subject.

Bob and Betty Brown likened these reports to a procedure of which they had heard carried on by the "Committees of Correspondence" which were started by Sam Adams in Boston, in November, 1772, and soon extending throughout New England, Virginia and other parts of the colonies led up to the plans for and the successful conduct of the War for Independence. The correspondence comprised a series of letters passed back and forth between different leaders in the colonies and proved to be a reliable means of keeping up contact between the great free men and at the same time in keeping the spark of patriotism aglow. Little was heard of the "Committees of Correspondence" but it became a historic institution in the story of the winning of independence for the colonies and the success of the early life of the Republic. The success of the "Committees of Correspondence" is a powerful testimonial in favor of the written or printed word as compared with the spoken word.

The Plan Team's operation consisted of less talk and more thinking, without any attempt on the part of one member of the loosely knit Team to sway the judgment of other members willing to work to improve a way of life at a remote place where none, except Achala and Mara, had any hope of participation.

Jim Welsh was a very astute thinker and more than did his part in supplying the ideas which the Team finally adopted to secure for the wage earner definite rights, protections, and privileges practically unheard of anywhere else in the world outside this little country. Uppermost in his mind was the thought that every wage earner must have an opportunity to advance to as high station in life as his abilities might merit. He resolved that he would maintain contact with the Team and did until many of his lifetime ambitions to obtain the utmost in rights and opportunities for wage earners were incorporated in the Alpaca Plan.

CHAPTER 8

ALPACANS STUDY THE PLAN

The Hani family were apart from the Achala family in that they were a more commercial clan and, while not opportunists, they were careful to refrain from alienating leaders of government in Alpaca, or any other country in which they transacted business.

The Hanis were not pro-dictator; they only wanted to get along, and would welcome any change in government as long as it was for the better, and would tolerate any change of government even if it were for the worse.

Mara, who had studied music abroad and entered on a brilliant career, was the apple of their eye. They preferred to think of her as their own and were not elated with her romance. They did recognize the Achalas for their fine traits, and all that they learned of the distinguished Juan Achala, they came to accept in his favor.

Mara was very influential with them as she began electioneering or propagandizing them in favor of the Alpaca plan. Following the marriage, to which the elder Hanis voiced no objection, they quietly but unmistakably began leaning toward a reform in government. A great advantage could come from their unofficial espousal of governmental reforms. The extreme practicability which was a part of the Hani nature was of inestimable value in effecting the reforms. They studied the Constitution, as one by one the provisions were sent by Mara from Europe, keeping uppermost in their minds the workability of its provisions, weighing the ease against the difficulty with which they could be effectuated.

They conveyed to Mara the glad word, which she passed on to Achala, that the Hanis could be counted on but asked that the information be handled confidentially.

An increasing number of people in Alpaca, regardless of the state of literacy, were now studying the Plan and its various provisions, as the Team sent drafts to Alpaca. In this great national discussion, people turned to the printed word rather than the oratorical demagogue. Literate Alpacans read the Plan to those who could not read, and innumerable small groups, always numbering fewer than 700, permitted by the Plan if adopted, met together to study and discuss the provisions in which they were most interested.

Considerable resistance in the Alpaca discussion groups to the delegation of voting power sprang up. Many declared that in cases where officers had duties only in the precinct, it would be preferable to vote for them directly instead of through delegates. It was argued that since citizens dealt directly with such officials, they should elect them directly. This called for a close study of the flexibility of their right.

They learned that, with a two-thirds majority vote, they could amend the Constitution as to their precinct, and vote directly to fill the offices within the precinct and if they did not like the change they could, with a simple majority, vote to return to the method provided in the Constitution.

The Senate consists of three Senators from each of the forty (40) legislative districts, each casting the aggregate voting power of his district. In Alpaca there is only one house in the Legislature—the unicameral system, as in Nebraska, USA, and elsewhere. This Legislative body considers legislation on its merit instead of being influenced by thought of what the other house may do where there is an upper and lower house. In Alpaca the legislators are free from the President's displeasure since the veto power is vested in a legislative veto board of three experienced legislators or statesmen with no "must" axes to grind and with no favors to withhold or to grant. One house can transact the legislative duties in half the time required by two houses. The veto power being vested in the Legislative Branch maintains the desired separation of the branches of government about which so much is heard and so little found.[7]

The ineligibility to succeed himself precludes the Senator from starting a campaign for re-election the day he is elected to his high position of trust.

A senatorial district has all of Alpaca from which to choose in electing its Senator and has no reason to select a soliciting, favor-seeking missionary for whatever "pork" he can bring home. Antonio Da Vinci, of all persons, supplied the information that the choice of a legislator from outside the district he would represent was a legal and common practice in England. Sir Gerald, when reached, quickly confirmed and expanded Antonio's statement. Combined with the investigations which had gone on before, this late advice was conclusive. An added incentive was furnished by Bob Brown, who pointed out that, while in practice, it is a dead issue, nothing in the U.S.A. Constitution requires a member of the lower house of Congress to be a resident of the District from which he is elected.

The Senate shall exercise diligence in keeping its Chairmanship filled as the chairman has many important duties of cooperation with other branches of government, but he would be relieved of the irksome duties arising from the conduct of sessions by being permitted to employ trained personnel, presiding officers, parliamentarians, *et cetera,* who are not elected members but possess the particular qualifications which better enable them to serve in their capacities than could the elected members. The special personnel, employed to assist in expediting sessions, are limited to individuals of 70 or less years, so that the post would never become an honorary sinecure, manned by citizens beyond the age of high competency.

---

[7]*Art. II, Secs. 1, 2, 3*

The rotation imposed for the Chairmanship precludes the buildup of the indispensable legislative man—a national idol able to destroy the government and the populace. Similar safeguards are set up in all other branches of the Government of Alpaca.

The true independence of the branches of government from each other, aside from occasional coordination through the National Policy Committee, has already become apparent. The Precinct delegates and candidates have the opportunity to specialize and devote their time and study to the particular branch of Government to which they are chiefly attracted. The things they have found out and their general knowledge are naturally and constantly communicated to their acquaintances, which results in an ever-increasing study of government and an informed and thinking people who, as they unselfishly learn the score, become intolerant of all dishonesty in government, intellectual or financial, and intolerant of pettifoggery, sham, deceit, sharp practices and subterfuge. Of their own knowledge the people will come to detect the counterfeit, the demagogue, the crank, the incompetent, and learn to respect the dependable, the prudent, and to form sound opinions as to the wisdom of the wise. The vital habit of vigilance is incubated by this entire process for all involved.

The independence of the Legislative Branch, which has steadily been undermined throughout the world by encroachment from the Executive Branch, and recently from the Judicial Branch, is amply protected in Alpaca. Other national figures attaining super roles in other branches of government, including the Military, might be under temptation to jeopardize the independence of the Legislative Branch were it not for the fact that they are wisely restrained and held in their place by provisions of the Alpaca Plan.

The Legislative Branch itself also would hold in check

its members and popular leaders to prevent them from reaching an undue prestige which would endanger the other branches of Alpacan government, including the Military. The safeguard is accomplished through rotation whereby no one in a top position in the Legislative or other branch of government is permitted to remain in his position long enough to build a personal following which might tempt him to seize Alpaca and exercise a dictatorial rule by man instead of the rule by law.

The Legislative Veto Board, having vital duties other than its right to veto laws enacted by the Senate, provides a throne of statesmanship to be found nowhere else in the world. The greatest of all former Senators, as well as Executives, Diplomats, Generals and Judges, could look forward to being elevated to such outstanding position, as long as they retained their utmost capacity and competency.[8]

The fewest laws, if adequate, make possible the finest legal structure. The judiciary and lawyers can best know the law when it is least complicated. The lay citizen desiring to be law-abiding has the best chance to fulfill his desire when there are fewer laws to be obeyed. The greatest of statesmen have repeatedly pointed out, "The best governed are the least governed."

With the twelve (12) year review of existing legislation, obsolete and redundant legislative enactments no longer clutter up the law books to confuse the Alpacan mind. Among the laws of highly civilized nations today could probably be found stern legislative acts to curb witchcraft and voodooism, in the thoroughly enforceable form, should public opinion become narrow-minded enough to require their enforcement.[9]

The work of some who contributed fine thinking and became nearly invaluable members of the Team can be credited

---

[8]*Art. II, Sec. 3*
[9]*Art. II, Sec. 4*

to Mara. There were some whom Achala could not enlist, great as was his winning personality and enthusiastic spirit. One of these was M. Andre Marchillon, the tax genius. Achala early heard of him and went to see him at his Versailles home, where he lived in retirement.

M. Marchillon listened with mild interest to Achala's enthusiastic narrative—it may have been amused interest. Alpaca meant little or nothing to this great Frenchman, who had repeatedly come to grips with the greatest tax problems of the greatest states and nations. He could easily understand the populace structure, visualize its people, but hardly knew where Alpaca was or why it was imperative that it have a new government. He could have asked himself, "But what shell of a country does not need a new body?"

But when the tax question became the uppermost problem of the Team, and when Mara, in Paris, knowing of M. Marchillon, called him on the 'phone, his interest in Alpaca took on an entirely different color. He was anxious to see for himself the parcel of femininity to which that mesmerizing voice was attached. After asking a few simple questions and finding there was no simple-mindedness in the answers, but vast understanding and great sweetness, he hurriedly invited Mara to drive over to see him. In answer to Mara's question "Whom shall I bring with me?" he dimly recalled the young man who, weeks before, had attempted to talk to him about Alpaca. He learned from Mara this young man's name and graciously extended an invitation—"If Achala can come, please bring him with you."

Only a short visit of the three completely changed the course of Marchillon's thinking and gave him a new attitude. He told Achala and Mara, "I have always wanted to outline a perfect tax structure but there has never been any reason for me to do so because it would never have been accepted by any country I have been called upon to serve." He added,

"This is entirely another situation. You, with your friends you have been telling me about, can do anything. You can accomplish the impossible and get something done right because it is right—simply an unheard-of occurrence in the annals of history."

The next day Marchillon was in Paris early, where he had access to actuary, statistical, clerical, and secretarial help, available to him at his call because of his known greatness and fine sincerity.

M. Marchillon proceeded at first with the Keynesian Theory propounded by Lord John Maynard Keynes, Director of the Bank of England until 1946, who dominated economic thinking after the Versailles Peace Treaty Conference at the end of World War I. Achala listened with rapt attention to the easy command of this great authority on the tax subject but found it difficult to follow the intricate thinking of Marchillon. He interrupted this great tax man to ask one very simple question.

"Do I understand, sir, that the raising of taxes necessarily has a deflationary effect?" M. Marchillon was on the verge of assuring this earnest young man with a question mark in his voice that such was the case, when suddenly a blank expression came over his face and to his own surprise found himself replying, "That may not be necessarily true. I thank you for raising the point; let us think this out together, let us see if it is often true or is ever true. I am beginning to see there can be a side that the best in our field have been overlooking."

He fell into deep thought and silence, which Achala did not interrupt, and in a few minutes M. Marchillon began talking continuously as though he were thinking aloud, which led those present to this summation:

A reasonable constancy of the value of the monetary unit is essential for national existence. Seldom, if ever, has the departure from the first established value of the unit been towards deflation. Deflation cannot destroy the value of a nation's money and inflation, unless sensibly held within restraint, must inevitably destroy it and destroy the nation.

Inflation is caused when there is more money and credit than goods, resulting in high prices and a decrease in the value of the monetary unit; deflation occurs in reverse. Conventional economists supposed that by imposing higher taxes, purchasing power would be decreased, and deflation, or lower prices, would result. But these economists were better acquainted with distribution than with production. They did not foresee the adverse effect which higher taxes would have upon production. As followers of the Keynesian theory of managed currency, they supposed that any economic problem could be solved merely by increasing or decreasing the monetary supply.

In countries which have adopted this remedy of higher taxes to halt inflation, the result has been more inflation. Higher taxes absorb some purchasing power, but they increase all costs of doing business, in production, transportation and distribution and again more high taxes on the resulting higher taxed product. This results in higher prices for everything, the very condition which higher taxes are intended to prevent. In every instance where this supposed remedy has been applied, higher taxes have become a self-feeding fire, increasing inflation. Another unexpected result was that higher taxes lowered the value of money, so that a given sum of money paid fewer taxes. In devising the tax structure for Alpaca, M. Marchillon took into account these unfortunate experiences of other countries who had tampered with their economies by using such poorly thought-out measures, and had reaped disastrous results.

From his vast experience and ability to think, he soon produced a tax structure which took into account all of the foibles of human nature familiar to him and all that he could anticipate.

After Achala's question to M. Marchillon had touched off a completely new trend of thought in working out the tax structure, the members of the Team regarded him with new respect.

After they had been advised by Marchillon, a new approach to the subject of taxation was made by decision of the Team, that tax limits, maximum and minimum, be specifically defined in the Constitution.

A table was presented in the Plan which not only guided and circumscribed the taxing power of the Senate, but also specified the avenues of taxation and their limits, pointed out the amount of taxation which can be imposed by the Senate to defray the costs of national existence, and defined the tax provisions for school districts, municipalities and special districts which could be set up, in the event that the acts establishing the special districts called for revenue from usual tax sources. Here arises a subject of such major importance, and so complicated, that the table of tax limits provided in the Constitution is herewith reproduced for convenient study.

The Senate shall establish an equitable and uniform system of taxation. The combined total of all taxes, national, school, municipal or special district except head tax and occupancy tax provided in Article II, Section 10 and Section 12, to prevent confiscation, shall be contained within the percentages of valuation as follows:

1. Annual Property Tax—fixed rate between ¾ of 1% and 1¼%

2. Import Tax — variable rate between 0% and 100%, depending on article

3. Export Tax — variable rate between 0% and 50%, depending on article

4. Severance Tax on Natural Resources — variable rate

between 0% and 30%, depending on article

5. Gift Tax — graduated rate from 0% to 15%

6. Inheritance Tax — graduated rate from 0% to 25%

7. Production or Manufacturing Tax — a fixed rate on each article

   (1) On luxury items, including alcoholic beverages and tobacco—fixed rate between 0% and 100%

   (2) On necessity items — fixed rate between 0% and 4%

8. Income Tax — graduated rate from 0% to 25%

9. Sales Tax — a fixed rate on each article

   (1) On luxury items, including alcoholic beverages and tobacco—fixed rate between 0% and 100%

   (2) On necessity items — fixed rate between 0% and 4%

10. Franchise Tax — fixed rate of 0% to 2% of volume of business

Tax exemptions for charitable and educational purposes have become a racket in many lands, because the charities frequently fall into the hands of enemies of Freedom who have skillfully gained control of charitable foundations and their assets, and the philanthropies of individuals, and who then direct the expenditures and distribution of these funds for the purpose of destroying or limiting human liberties; therefore, Achala proposed that these exemptions should be prescribed and curtailed.

In Alpaca, tax exemptions would not be permitted on any property owned or used by the Government; on property, resources or income used in philanthropies of any nature, except solely for advancing medical science, care of the sick, and public enlightenment to promote personal initiative and individual liberty. Contributions by individuals to religious institutions or through these to programs meeting these qualifications would be deductible up to thirty (30) per cent of the donor's income. The Constitution adequately identifies a religion to preclude an inventive pretense for tax purposes.

It was realized that assessing and collecting of taxes can become a nuisance to tax-collecting authorities as well as the taxpayer, if the amount collected is little more than the cost of its collection. Therefore, the wise provision was included that the assessments shall not be made against taxpayers of certain classes during the time that the cost of processing and collecting the tax from them would exceed 50% of the revenue to be collected. Behind the provision was the thought that the tax bite itself is obnoxious enough to the payee, and should be to those whose duty is to impose it, so that the pain of the bite should not be increased unnecessarily.

The tax provisions also banned withholding taxes, to be deducted from the payroll by the employer. The reasoning behind this stipulation was as follows:

Big taxes encourage overbearing and despoiling government, and government has been and always will be destructive to human liberty. Deductions from the payroll are a vicious tax, because they are so convenient to use in exacting a tax from the most modestly situated of the citizenry. If such withholding does not arouse resentment in the taxpayer, it is because it has become an invisible tax. The submissive taxpayer, broken to the yoke, soon learns to accept such withholding from his pay without protest, or if he resents it, he attributes it to the malice or oppression of his employer. The employer is made to appear a skinflint. He is forced into the role of an unwilling tax collector, and in the eyes of his employees he seems to be a sweatshop keeper or worse, no matter how excellent his record of upright citizenship.

While it may be thought ridiculous that it is necessary for the Constitution to recite that tax money shall not be assessed or spent except for authorized purposes, the Team felt that it should be included. Only the circumvention of constitutional government, written or unwritten, prevailing in highly civilized countries makes such recitals have any sense whatsoever.

CHAPTER 9

ROMANCE

Team members devoted so much time, thought, and energy to the engrossing task of ushering in a new era for Alpaca, that Sir Gerald, one day conferring with Achala and Mara, astonished them by suddenly laying down his pen, leaning back in his chair and saying, dramatically:

"Even Jove nods! Why shouldn't mortals relax occasionally?"

Achala smiled. "You mean we've been working too steadily?"

"Positively so!" Sir Gerald assured him with emphasis. "This strain is too absolutely terrific. Are we Platos, or are we not? I suggest that we pick up the Lady Arifa and go to Maxim's for refreshment and refueling, don't you know!"

"Dear Sir Gerald," said Mara soothingly. "A cup of coffee at a sidewalk cafe would do me worlds of good. I like to breathe the fresh air, watch the people go by."

So the four of them followed this suggestion. They fell to wondering as they watched strange faces, the shy and the bold, the gay and the sad, how many of these folk were informed; of those informed, which were constructives and which held liberalism as their goal.

"I think," said Mara, making a dainty choice from a dish of delicacies, "that France is a very lovable country. While I was here as a student, it hurt me to feel the very ground quake under my feet with every change of administration."

"At that time, Mara dear, you were thinking more about modulations from key to key," remarked Lady Arifa, who looked trim and complacent, having adapted speedily to her new role in life.

Mara contended, "I thought about both. Now that I am gaining better perspective, I long to be of use in stabilizing our own Alpacan government."

Her husband looked at her with pride, realizing anew the many bright facets of her personality.

Lady Arifa took a letter from her handbag, saying, "Mara, this is for you. It came to the old address." Mara scanned it quickly. "Just another offer from an agent. Let me examine the postmark."

"That reminds me," said Achala, "the next section we shall discuss is to be the postal system in Alpaca."

The constitutional draft, as Achala sent it to Alpaca, contained the interesting provision that the Senate could, if it believed it would benefit the nation, contract out the Alpaca postal system to privately owned companies.[10]

Some of Achala's advisors had constantly urged for nationalization of various industrial activities. One of the questions they used as a clinching argument was, "How could postal systems be operated if governments did not do it?" Achala's apt answer was, it has never been proved that government should not let contracts to private enterprises, to attain the most efficient and economical conduct of the postal service. It has been repeatedly proved, throughout the world, that private ownership in one industry after another is more economical and efficient than government ownership and operation. In spite of improved air service, government subsidies to airlines and all the vast technological improvements which have become available to transmission of mail in recent years, the postal service in many countries is constantly deteriorating. It often takes nearly twice as long for the addressee to receive a letter as the transmission of such a letter required only a few years ago, and the cost of postage required is constantly being stepped up.

Impatient with hearing thoughtless expressions frequently repeated, Josef said to Achala, "There is too much printed

---

[10]*Art. II, Sec. 6*

matter going through the mails anyway. If people would only read! The things they hear only mislead them — the things they read they can look over twice, or several times, if needed. How can we get people to read? In the course of human events they even fail to read their insurance policies for which they have paid. They will not read the fine lines and find out what is in the policies upon which they are depending when the time of travail and misfortune arrives." Achala, resourceful though he was, had no sure cure to offer.

In addition to the Senate's duty to provide the control of crime, to adopt rules of criminal procedure, and to regulate foreign commerce, Achala's draft further requires that the Senate appropriate adequate funds for the military and other governmental bodies. This requirement precludes any attempt by the Senate to control or dominate the military, a department which must always remain free from the dictate or control of any one branch of the government. The Team realized that constant vigil should be exercised against the possibility that a "strong man" in the government might use the military to seize control and to break up the system of checks and balances so adequately provided in the Constitution, and against any attempt of such a "strong man," either self-righteously or selfishly, to assume dictatorial power over the people.

In the Plan, Achala had accepted M. Marchillon's admonition that the economy should not be tied to the gold standard. The Plan instead provides that the currency should be redeemable in wheat, rice and other commodities; in other words, a commodity Pack rather than a gold Pack. Governmental obligations are held to a fixed valuation at home, but at three-year intervals, or longer, they could be changed to conform with world inflation or deflation. The redemption pledge in commodities affords definite values, whereas if the currency were redeemable in gold, necessity might require the temporary abandonment of the gold standard, and such an expediency could become permanent.[11]

For ages there were vital uses for gold, nearly all of which have been supplanted as a result of improved metallurgy, use of plastics and other materials; but as far as known, people will continue to wish and will need to eat.

The Team proposed that the Government make available designated redemption points where Packs in the form of currency could be converted into commodities, within twenty days of notice given by the holders of the currency. The 1/100th to 1/4th subdivisions of the Pack are in coin, redeemable only in paper Pack and not in commodities.

The quality of Alpacan citizenship was zealously guarded in the Plan. The Senate was clothed with the responsibility of enacting laws regulating immigration, with rules for the naturalization of self-supporting aliens who lawfully reside in Alpaca. The need of the requirement that aliens be self-supporting and law abiding has become increasingly recognized throughout the world. It was provided that the naturalized Alpacan citizen must forego allegiance to any foreign country, the penalty for failure being revocation of Alpacan citizenship and deportation. Should acts of treason to Alpaca be proved, the prescribed penalty for treason takes precedence over deportation.[12]

Mara, not yet divorced from the atmosphere of art, recalled stray words and happenings in her recent experience, which deepened the channel of her work in the Plan.

She had been interested in the places where it was expected her career would lead her. There was the chance remark by an agent from the great Opera House in Buenos Aires. He had made a study of the situation and assured her that the illegal aliens scattered throughout the world are numbered in the

---

[11]*Art. II, Sec. 7*
[12]*Art. II, Sec. 8*

millions. They are often hosts to or sometimes become part and parcel of a Fifth Column, infiltrating many countries as agents for aggressor nations; they are to be found residing or "visiting" in strategic places. They are there to practice espionage; to entice and enlist gullibles and dupes; they consort with intellectuals to build and join subtle organizations intended to pave the way for the overthrow of their host government. These organizations assume the most patriotic names in the nation and are generally announced to be of a charitable nature. They are planned so that the highly civic-minded easily fall for them. When the appropriate moment shall arrive in the minds of the master planners, they will be ready to help deliver the *coup de grace*. They are the bitter fruit of unrestricted immigration and carelessly administered immigration laws.

Moreover, as Mara reflected in a flash of analysis, there are in all these countries native sons and daughters of impeccable reputation and vast resources, with fanatical philosophies which make them traitors to their homelands, to whom the aliens look for crafty guidance. These strangely minded citizens work up into high positions in public relations, public affairs, education and religion. Under them, and sometimes with them, the aliens toil indefatigably for the national ruin and the ruin of all that these queer citizens are supposed to hold dear.

Truly, thought she, to oppose such misguided fanatics is better even than to sing the music of Mozart and Verdi. In line with Mara's views, the Constitution places the Senate under mandate to regulate the residence and potential citizenship of aliens and makes Alpaca citizens abroad subject to the Nation's laws until citizenship is relinquished.

The special requirements of local government are also provided. Situations might arise in which the residents of some areas might seek a special law applicable only to that area.

The Senate would give consideration to the need for such special legislation which would have to conform to the law of Alpaca. If granted, it would be in effect a National Law for a specific area and become effective only after a majority vote of acceptance by the Precinct Legislative Delegates representing that area.[13]

The need for the creation of such districts, perhaps in a river valley or a forest range, is difficult to foresee in advance of a request for them. The situation would be simple in handling if it did not involve special and additional taxes. When such a step would be deemed necessary, in the judgment of the Legislators, the creation of a Special District could be constitutional.

No nation is stronger than the educational system which trains its future citizenry. Provision is made in the Plan for compulsory education for children from six through 14 years of age, and the parents and guardians are held responsible for each child's attendance. The six-year age minimum is subject to an exception suggested by the recognized success of the Maria Montessori method. If children of three and four years in kindergarten can pass examinations that evidence qualification to enter grades with children of over five years, their parents have the right to place them in such higher grades. The plan for school elections and taxes necessary to maintain schools is provided in conformity with the laws of Alpaca, with school officials directly concerned with each school in charge of policies, administration, control and raising of the necessary funds. The government makes the requirement that the annual salary of teachers and instructors in the educational field shall exceed by thirty percent the highest average pay of the best paid unskilled hourly or per diem wage earner in the area. The latter is a wise provision to overcome the

---

[13]*Art. II, Sec. 9*

inadequate pay for teachers which prevails throughout the world.[14]

Teachers exercise a great influence in the lives of the young, and unless teachers thrive in an atmosphere of freedom, they can develop a dangerous complex: preferring that freedom be cast aside and that individual liberty be subjugated in favor of any ism which holds out to them a false hope for a higher station in life. Free governments must be zealous in tangibly bringing home to the teachers that the achievement of a better life for themselves under free institutions is more than an empty distant promise.

The provision for local government was implicit. It was specified that municipalities must first look for support to occupancy and franchise taxes. Should these prove inadequate, they can then draw upon the unused portions of taxes provided for national government and schools in the same order that they are provided in the tax table. It may be that the first use of income taxes and sales taxes will arise in municipal taxation.[15]

---

[14]*Art. II, Sec. 10, 11*
[15]*Art. II, Sec. 12*

CHAPTER 10

THE EXECUTIVE TRIUMVIRATE

Achala and Mara had quizzed Jim Welsh, the Browns, Antonio, and other teammates on the subject of which they were themselves least familiar. They knew employees but in a different status from that generally spoken of as "Labor." As a result of their studies they proposed something entirely new in the field of labor thought.

Working has always been a means of sustenance. The application of effort in some form today remains a necessity for life except for those with inherited and accumulated fortunes. Except for the rich, the individual without the right to work has no actual rights and can even, through circumstances, be deprived of the right to life. Achala framed his provisions under these premises.[16]

The enforceable legal rights provided wage earners give them, in fact, all of the rights which demagogues and malefactors can picture for them through glib and false promises. The sacred right to work is guaranteed each citizen, and the Senate shall enact proper legislation providing for the enforcement of legal rights for wage-earning persons, providing these rights from employers: disability pay for injuries; vacations with pay; to accept bonuses from employers when offered; to be paid the Wage and Hour Commission minimum wage, and to accept for better workmanship or greater efficiency higher pay than the average wage for the same tasks; to be afforded healthful working conditions together with recreational and entertainment facilities; to freedom from abuse by word or deed; to be free from paying a fee to the employers or any other person or organization as a condition for obtaining and continuing a job. The Senate is precluded from attempting to endow

---

[16]*Art. II, Sec. 13*

the wage earner with rights which are impractical of fulfillment, such as a property right in his job, a right to take over his employer's property, or to force the employer to guarantee a wage in the future whether or not the employee works. Unemployment insurance also falls within this class. These enforceable legal rights for a wage worker would not provide the protection they do were it not for the fact that the worker has easy and inexpensive access to labor courts, where his rights can be adjudicated and enforced. This also protects the employer from being forced to suspend his activities at the whim of others, and at the same time insures to the wage earner his vital right to quit a job in orderly procedure.

The privilege of an employee to terminate his job is provided in the Constitution, and this sacred right to quit work cannot be taken away from him in the guise of a violation of the public welfare, or in the name of "national emergency" as has occurred frequently in ancient and modern countries. To protect this right, the Constitution provides that the only requirement for an employee to quit is to give the employer notice, which the employer must honor by naming the time of termination, at the minimum of 8 percent each day of the total staff of the employer at the date of notice or in any event within 14 days from the receipt of notice. The employer shall give a preference for length of service in apportioning the time of termination from the employees from whom he has received notice of their desire to quit. Without this protection to the wage earner, Alpaca could become, for many, a land of peonage.

The stature of a people may be judged by their concern for their sick. The greatest humanitarians with whom Achala and Mara talked were concerned over the problem of ample hospitalization for the sick. A program was sought which could make Alpaca a great health center, while avoiding welfare-state practices and nationalization of the medical profession. It was finally decided that the government should accredit non-governmental hospitals and should build additional facilities for the care of the sick, ample to care for ten percent in excess of the average number of sick, when and where needed, and furnish these facilities free of cost to the most efficient organizations or staffs which can be found to operate and maintain them. These organizations may be medical associations, charitable bodies, or concerns operating with profit as their motive.[17] The custodians of the hospitals will make proper charges against those who can pay or have other arrangements for paying their hospital expenses, and will extend a reasonable amount of charity. Care is taken to avoid the nationalizing of the medical profession, which has been tried and proved a failure in many lands.

Quite naturally, Mara, more than anyone else of the Plan Team, was concerned with the fate of orphans. After a great amount of discussion the simplest provisions seemed to be the best, and these were briefly but adequately set forth in Section 15:

> The Senate shall enact legislation providing for appropriate facilities for the care of orphans and adoption procedures and agencies for all orphans.[18]

Achala and Mara found that all with whom they talked showed a deep interest in the role which government might play in business. It was decided to keep the government out of competition with private business and to keep government holdings at the lowest level possible. Private citizens have the right to sue the government for losses which they suffer at the hands of the government, when the government pre-empts from them property which they need

---

[17]*Art. II, Sec. 14*
[18]*Art. II, Sec. 15*

and should be permitted to own.[19]

Rules for the operation of the Senate were included in the Plan. The Senate is required to function in a workmanlike manner and to avoid the closing legislative log jams that have become an undignified procedure in legislative halls throughout the world, offering a temptation for some members to make trades and deals for the support of one measure in order to obtain support for another. The Chairman of the Senate shall impose cloture, limiting each member to two hours of speech, debate or time taken by him interrupting other speakers in considering a legislative act. Actual results and majority rule subject to veto are much better than delaying tactics and stagnation. A final vote is required on each measure within ten days after it comes to the Senate floor. These arrangements represent a more advanced approach to the enactment of legislation than has been achieved in any other nation.[20]

When an emergency meeting of the Senate is needed, the discretionary power to call the members into special session is lodged in the Chairman of the Senate, or the National Policy Committee. Regular sessions are called by the Chairman.

Achala had been so impressed by the evils of bureaucracy abroad that he persuaded his co-workers to declare war against bureaucracy in Alpaca. He knew, from his study of history that the excessive and cancerous growth of bureaucracy had weakened or destroyed many governments, especially the Byzantine Empire in the fourteenth century, and later on other countries which inherited the methods of the Byzantine bureaucracy. The Byzantine Empire had lasted for twelve centuries which was longer than any other empire in the history of the world, yet in the end it was devoured by bureaucracy.

---

[19]*Art. II, Sec. 16*
[20]*Art. II, Secs. 17, 18*

Bureaucracy is a self-created and self-perpetuated malignancy which continues to grow at the expense of the constructive elements of the nation, until at last it chokes off and destroys orderly process. The Plan Team effected safeguards against the evils of bureaucracy by the provisions requiring the termination after eighteen months of all bureaus set up on a temporary basis and providing that the usefulness of permanent bureaus be subject to constant review and checkup, with requirement that they be dismantled when feasible. Alpaca could not hope to endure for long without Section 20.[21]

Suffrage for women had been agreed upon from the very start. To clarify the property rights of the wife, Section 21 was agreed upon, closely following the best-working community property ownership laws which could be found in the experience of other nations.[22]

The organization of the Executive Department confronted the Team with probably their most difficult decision. The presidential office in all republics, or democracies, has always offered a danger spot from which ambitious men could step out of bounds and into dictatorship. It was decided to set up an Executive Triumvirate limiting the President of Alpaca to a status as annual head of the Triumvirate, the other two members being First and Second Assistants. It had frequently been said and proved that the presidency is too big a job for one man; that it is a killer; that it requires seclusion and protection which destroys the common touch. Although these truths have been recognized since the days of ancient Roma, no logical effort has been made to do anything about it until the Plan of the present Alpaca.[23]

Alpaca's solution went to the heart of the Chief Executive problem. The President's burdens are lightened by the pres-

---

[21]*Art. II, Sec. 20*
[22]*Art. II, Sec. 21*
[23]*Art. III, Sec. 1*

ence of two assistants, each performing some of his functions, and at the same time preparing to take over the duties of President at the end of either one or two years. They may preside or sit in at Cabinet sessions, grant audiences to the key men in the Executive Branch, study budgets, and assist the President in all matters. The people are fortunate at all times in having elected representatives in these vital positions.

Through this imaginative conception, Alpaca finds adequate protection against the emergence of the indispensable man. Herein lies the extreme danger of a sole national leader becoming a popular idol who, building up a blind following, could destroy the nation and its people, or nullify the precepts which they hold dear: as had happened in Germany, Italy and many other places where otherwise happiness would abound.

The Chief Executive is more prone than the head of any other department to form "kitchen cabinets," to enjoy court jesters, and to permit the building of a coterie of favorites, often spoken of as "insiders." In this agglomeration may be found mistaken idealists, large or small grafters, or some one all-powerful intimate, even a Rasputin.

A helpful team member, stolid, thrifty Hans Kyle from Bonn, volunteered this interesting story. He had taken upon himself a study of the sway of Rasputin and gave Achala and Mara a recital of the activities of this unbelievable character.

Rasputin is not to be described as the typical favorite of an Executive, but of interest as an extreme case. He was a discredited, almost illiterate Greek Orthodox monk, who claimed sometimes to be divinely inspired and was shrewd enough to maintain such evil influence on the ruler of the country that a whisper or a hint from him became law.

Rasputin proved to be very tenacious; he outlived an attempt to poison him with a strong dose of potassium cyanide in wine. On December 17, 1916, three months before the regime he had brought into disrepute was overthrown, he was finally liquidated, being shot, stabbed, and then submerged in a river, by a group of noblemen.

It became increasingly apparent that the damage Rasputin had done was beyond repair and the centuries-old Tsarist regime crumbled and fell, never to be restored.

State Executives have seldom gone so far as to use, or be used by, a Rasputin. But the power of intimates is often allowed to exceed their own. Hans' face wore a very worried expression as he declared solemnly:

"Too often such favorites are selected because of whim or because they have some irregular or abnormal characteristics. Few have gone down in history as good influences; in the large majority of cases the control they exert is bad, and detrimental to the nation which the Executive, however chosen, is pledged to serve to the best of his ability and wise judgment."

If suffering mortals could have only had unexcitable or unpopular leaders who were kept in office simply because they were doing a good job, the Triumvirate system of Alpaca would still be needed, but not so urgently. It is a foolproof system. Should the presidency somehow go to a complete misfit, the Nation would still have a workable team of three (3) who could care for the imperative executive duties until a reluctant Investigating Committee and Vacancy Board, forced to deal with the top office, would be able to correct the mistake and replace the misfit.

CHAPTER 11

THE JUDICIARY

Switzerland has proved at least twice in the past 44 years that there is no leader wise enough to decide which war his country should get into. It is interesting to ask, by the way, who is well enough posted to remember who was the national leader of that complacent, prosperous country from 1914 to 1918 and from 1938 to 1945. Remember? You do not remember. Over-advertised national heroes are often dangerous and expensive luxuries.

The Team early became aware that its members and those whom they visited all thought that they were quite well informed about the Government of Switzerland, but in trying to answer a few simple questions were forced to admit that they knew very little about it. They decided that the same is probably true of the general public throughout the world. In their embarrassment they turned to their good Swiss friend, Emil Strube. As usual, he proved extremely helpful by contributing his views as to the relevance of Swiss measures to the Alpaca plan.

Switzerland began taking form August 1, 1291, as a defensive league. In 1798, under the influence of France, it became the Helvetic Republic. Napoleon Bonaparte, in 1803, in the Act of Mediation, installed a new Constitution and increased the Cantons to 19 in number. In 1815, the perpetual neutrality of Switzerland was guaranteed by Austria, France, Great Britain, Portugal, Prussia, Russia, Spain and Sweden. In 1848, a new Constitution was passed without foreign interference. Alpacans can hope that this same freedom will come true for them. This in turn was, in 1874, superseded by the Constitution which is now in force. It may be revised either by federal legislation with compulsory referendum or upon the demand of 50,000 voters, a majority both of the citizens voting and of the Cantons. Constitutions, to endure, must be subject to amendments. It occurred to Emil that the Team could improve this provision for Alpaca. The Supreme legislative authority of Switzerland is vested in a Parliament of two Houses, the first composed of 44 members chosen by the Cantons, now twenty-two in number; the mode of election and term depending on the Canton. The 196 members of the second House are chosen in a direct election, each for four years at the rate of one deputy for every 24,000 people. Every male citizen, 21 years or older, is entitled to vote and any voter not a clergyman may be elected a deputy.

Laws passed by both chambers may be vetoed by a "yes" or "no" referendum held at the request of 30,000 citizens of 8 Cantons. "Not nearly so good as our Plan," gently opined Emil.

Chief Executive authority is the Federal Council consisting of seven members, elected from seven different Cantons for four years in a joint session of both chambers. Members of this Council may not hold any other office, or engage in any other calling or business. Federal Legislation may be introduced either by a member of either House or by the Federal Council. The President and the Vice President of the Federal Council, members of the Federal Council, are elected by the members of the Federal Assembly of both Houses by a joint vote for a term of one year and are ineligible to the same offices until after the expiration of another year. The Vice President may be and usually is elected to succeed the outgoing President. The President is, but not always, spoken of as President of the Swiss Confederation, leading some persons to sometimes think they have none. "The Alpaca Triumvirate and rotation plan is as good — only better," volunteered Emil.

The Federal Tribunal, which sits at Lausanne, consists of 26-28 members, with 11-13 supplementary judges, appointed by the Federal Assembly for six years and eligible for re-election; the President and Vice President, as such, hold office for two years and cannot be re-elected. These titles confuse the outsider's mind as to the Swiss National Presidency, or lack of it. Jurors are elected in many Cantons. This is a step in the right direction toward the trained commissioners sitting in with Judges to render decisions in Alpacan Courts.

Communes, ranging from fourteen up to a few thousand persons, comprise the Cantons.

The administration of the Swiss Army is partly in the hands of the Cantonal Authority, which can promote officers up to the rank of Captain. All the higher appointments are made by the Federal Government. In peacetime, the Swiss Army has no General; only in time of war the Federal Assembly appoints a full-time General.

Emil gently implied that the secret for peace was a widely based government, the presidency limited to one year, and the absence of any general in time of peace to promote a demand for military action. The Swiss attend to their own business and charge outsiders handsomely for attending to theirs. Switzerland has recently passed "welfare" laws, the outcome to be watched as in all other nations.

Achala and Mara had given much thought to the question of obtaining civil servants of the highest qualifications. They had rejected the concept of a Civil Service which, in highly advanced countries, has only too often degenerated into a device to freeze spiritless and mediocre employees into immovable job tenure. Civil Service in its operation is a continuing feeder to inflation, hotbed of inefficiency, and a national extravagance. The Team came up with the new concept of an Examining Board. The Examining Board screens prospective appointees to the Executive Branch of Government. It is elected by the delegates. The Chief of the Board has other important functions in the Government.[24]

It is the duty of the Board to maintain close contact with graduates from high schools and colleges who have taken governmental training courses. It assists in keeping efficiency and background records of all applicants under consideration. The Board does not attempt to bind the elected executive in making his appointments, but should he make an improper or mistaken appointment, it has the authority to reject it.

Thus the Board exercises the confirmation authority which, in such a nation as the USA, is lodged in its upper House, where this august body has substantially abdicated its duties to reject appointments, and for all practical purposes has become a rubber stamp of the President of the USA. Differing from the USA the confirmation of appointments by the Executive is confined to the Executive Department, and the separation of the four branches of government is here as in all situations maintained in Alpaca.

The Plan has a fresh approach to the subject of treaties with foreign nations. It proposes the unique instrumentality of a Treaty Committee. Treaties become binding only when ratified by a majority of the Committee. Through this device, the President, in negotiating treaties, can be aware at all times whether or not the treaty he is contemplating will be ratified.[25]

By such consultation with the Treaty Committee, whose members are the Chairman of the Senate, the Chief Justice of the Supreme Court, and the Chief of the Examining Board of the Executive Department, Alpaca is able to attain stability in its foreign policy, and afford popular understanding of its purposes.

This will forestall the evils which might come from Summit conferences with its little neighbors. The wise provision

[24]*Art. III, Sec. 2*
[25]*Art. III, Sec. 3*

in this clause is that a treaty when consummated would not become a precedent in law, thus having little impact on domestic law. The need of limiting the treaty-making power of the Executive is thus avoided.

Young Victor of Belgium, who was a part-time wage earner, part-time student, and full-time thinker, learned of the Plan Team through Jim Welsh. Victor was concerned with the unemployment situation, or, as he preferred to discuss it, the full-time employment program. It served little purpose for the worker to look forward to full time if he were to be paid only a starvation wage. "FULL-TIME WITH A MINIMUM WAGE" was Victor's slogan, and his solicitude in this respect was not selfish, for he had no doubt that he would soon rise to a station wherein he would be unemployed, because he would be his own boss.[26]

Through the report of Jim Welsh and Robert Brown, and Victor's thinking, Achala had reached a cure for "boom or bust" economy through the proposed Wage and Hour Commission, empowered to make a continuous study of the amount of work which is needed to be done, and the number of workers available to do it. This Commission reports its findings to the National Policy Committee, which will issue directives for a prescribed number of hours as the work week. This enables the Policy Committee, effectively and simply, to prevent all abnormal unemployment.

Such an elimination of unemployment will spread purchasing power uniformly, and this should prove to be the cure for all depressions without in any way jockeying with the value of the monetary unit or tinkering with credit. It will also make the need of unemployment insurance nil, for the work to be done is well spread among those who want to work. The National Policy Committee is empowered to set a minimum wage for males and minimum wage for

---

[26]*Art. III, Sec. 4*

females.

In case a national emergency should necessitate a considerable increase in the national work load, the work week could be lengthened by the National Policy Committee so that the available workers could get a greater amount of work performed, smoothly and adequately, without inflicting hardship on management, wage earners, and the public.

Achala and Mara, learning of punishments meted out in Paris to members of the Armed Forces of other nations stationed in France, were concerned for the future of the Alpaca military. They provided a section giving legal protection to members of the Armed Forces serving on foreign soil.[27] They were actuated by the belief that if servicemen are not to be protected, they should not be asked to serve. Failure to act promptly whenever possible, when Alpacans' rights are violated in other countries, would make a laughing stock of the Armed Forces and discredit the nation's integrity.

In dealing with the Judicial Branch of the government, the Team was advised by Orlando Tasso, the great Italian authority on International Law. They set up a Supreme Court of nine Justices, making them responsible for the establishment and assigning of duties of lower courts without delegating to the Supreme Court authority to name those who would serve in the lower courts. The Chief Justice, being one of the highest officials of the Alpacan Government, would be limited to serving as Chief Justice for a period of two years, and, although continuing on the Court, he would be ineligible to serve as Chief Justice again until the lapse of one year. All members of the Supreme Court, other than the initial members, must have had previous judicial experience, for they would be required to

---

[27]*Art. III, Sec. 5*

have previously served as judges in courts for a period of four years or more.[28]

In the place of the usual jury system in the lower courts, the Plan provides a system of two elected commissioners who act as associates with the judge in hearing cases and in rendering verdicts, all of which would be subject to appeal. Judges of the lower National Courts and two Commissioners similarly elected could render unanimous, or two to one verdicts, and if none of the three should agree, the judge alone would be empowered to render the verdict, all verdicts being subject to appeal.[29]

Provision was made for labor judges to afford complainants, either employees or employers, easy and inexpensive hearings as to the right of the complainants, the verdict being subject to appeal. The procedures have been described in the discussion of Article II, Section 13.[30]

The Team dispensed with the time-honored right of the defendant to a trial by a presumably impartial jury of his peers. Many European and South American countries, as well as the USA, had adopted the jury system as the cornerstone of justice. However, the use of juries in these countries is slightly waning. The Jury System is expensive and slow, and jury duty is regarded as very onerous by most citizens who are asked to serve. The best of the panel summoned are usually challenged by attorneys for defendants and seldom accepted to hear a case; hence, few of the jurors eventually chosen can clearly comprehend the evidence and the legal points involved. Among the large number of jurors, a few become targets to "fix" through influence or the object of attempted bribery for the purpose of "hanging the jury." In Alpaca, the two commissioners, sitting with the judge in hearing and deciding a

[28]*Art. IV, Secs. 1, 2*
[29]*Art. IV, Sec. 3*
[30]*Art. IV, Sec. 4*

case, are known to possess legal knowledge, as they are elected by the delegates who in turn have been chosen by the people for their aptitude in the legal branch, and the verdict is subject to appeal. The procedures have been described in the discussion of Article II, Section 13. Jurors are elective in some Swiss Cantons.

The Supreme Court is required to establish Appellate Courts composed of three elected judges.[31]

Seven Supreme Court affirmative votes are required to declare an Act of the Senate unconstitutional and six affirmative votes are required to nullify actions taken by the Executive. The Constitution can be amended only as provided in Article VI. This curbs the court from attempting to enact legislation by judicial decree, and contains the unusual provision that if the Supreme Court is uncertain of the Senate's intent in enacting a law, it is proper for the Court to request the Senate to enact new legislation clarifying its intent. The Supreme Court is not permitted to decide the intent of the Senate.[32]

---

[31]*Art. IV, Sec. 5*
[32]*Art. IV, Sec. 6*

CHAPTER 12

MILITARY AND SENIORITY

Those drafting the Plan were highly concerned with the Military Branch of the government. After long study, they reached the following conclusions: To make the office of the Commander-in-Chief of the Armed Forces, in which all branches of the Military are united, a rotating position. The Commander-in-Chief can serve only two consecutive years. This is a precaution to prevent his development into a national hero whose accumulated prestige could do great harm. He is responsible for the Armed Forces, but is subordinate to the National Policy Committee, composed of the President, Chief Justice and Chairman of the Legislative Veto Board. The arrangement gives security against the danger that the Commander-in-Chief get out of hand or divert the military into the hands of some other over-ambitious "strong man" in government.

The Commander-in-Chief and the National Policy Committee conduct foreign military actions, but in addition must secure the consent of the Chairman of the Senate to use military forces to police internal areas.[33]

The military delegates would be apart from the general electoral machinery of Alpaca. The intent of the military delegate system is to prevent the officers of the armed forces from becoming an autonomous power, parallel to the civilian government, which could be manipulated by unscrupulous government heads to destroy the Constitution. The history of most dictatorships and tyrannies is a chronicle of usurpation of authority by a military power above and beyond the law.

Alpaca's way of dealing with this danger is to interpose civilian influence in the intermediate and highest ranks of

---

[33]*Art. V, Sec. 2*

the officer corps, in addition to short-term rotation of the head of the military command. In the Alpaca army, the three top officers are elected by the highest college of military delegates.

The office of Commander-in-Chief rotates among the three at intervals of two years. In top policy matters the Commander-in-Chief is responsible, not to the Executive, as in other countries, but to the National Policy Committee, which represents all three government branches.

Below the top rank, all offices above that of Captain are filled by vote of the military delegates, with the exception of divisional commanders and top staff members, who are named by the Commander-in-Chief. Lower officers and non-commissioned officers ranging upward from Corporal to Captain, or equivalent, are named by the intermediate officers. Thus the civilian voice is decisively heard in the total conduct of the armed forces. The composition of the military delegates, as far as possible, differs from the composition of the other delegate groups. Preferably, ex-servicemen and present members of the armed forces are elected to such delegateships, although civilians with knowledge of military affairs will be sought for nomination. As an added safeguard against army usurpation, the Plan bars members of the armed forces from holding any other post in the government. With a few specified exceptions, military officers serve without limit as long as they are able.

Volunteers will be accepted and conscription used when necessary, with equal pay for both. If the Nation should find it necessary to appropriate private property, the owner will be reimbursed for full value. Large military establishments will not be maintained, since in modern warfares scientists are more important than numbers. The slingshot, crossbow, rifle, machinegun and heavy artillery are outmoded. The men who could be killed by opposing forces are not needed. New devices are so destructive that lengthy war, in its historical form, is probably a thing of the past.[34]

Achala's proposed method of promptly amending the Constitution is a guarantee against ill-considered action. Amendments may be submitted by a two-thirds vote of the Senate, or by a unanimous vote of the National Policy Committee. They would become effective when approved by a two-thirds vote of all delegates chosen in the precinct at the next general election or at a special election held within two years of submission.[35]

The Team gave much thought to the question of abuses in the operation of government. They felt that investigation and publicity were not enough if the investigating body did not have the power of dismissal. Accordingly, they proposed the election of an investigating committee of nine by the top college of each branch of government.[36] Such a committee, they felt, thanks to its permanent character, will function more efficiently than the sporadic investigations carried on by the British "Royal Commissions" or the investigating sub-committees of the USA Congress. Their findings will carry convincing prestige. These are responsible committees with authority to suspend the occupant of any position. Such a Committee, with its broad powers, could become a vicious body. However, since the committees are composed of highly intelligent, high-minded men, chosen by responsible delegates, it is unthinkable that they will have any incentive to suspend or remove any person unjustly from a position. Moreover, such injustice would have to be perpetrated in connivance with the Vacancy Committee, also elective, which would have the sole power to fill the vacancy they had created. The supposition

----

[34]*Art. V, Sec. 4*
[35]*Art. VI, Sec. 2*
[36]*Art. VII, Sec. 1*

that two small bodies, so carefully chosen, would go off the beam simultaneously and join each other in an act in violation of the confidence which had been placed in them, is extremely unlikely.

In the earlier discussion of Article I, Section 8, the reasons for adopting the Vacancy Committee plan and its procedure have pointed up the wisdom of this provision.

Penalties of imprisonment for three or more years, or death, are provided for acts of treason.[37]

The Plan declared that anyone being paid funds from the government, including salaried personnel, would not be deemed innocent until proved guilty, and would be discontinued from government activities upon substantial charges until such time as their innocence has been proved. This develops one of the finest thoughts to be found in the Constitution. This provision, had it been in force in other countries, would have prevented the horrors of an official carrying on acts of treason even after becoming suspected of subversion.[38]

Some of Achala's elders had impressed upon him that the citizenry generally may not in their productive years situate themselves favorably for their life in their advanced years. After exhausting all available information on the subject, the Team drafted a uniform seniority payment provision as a substitute for the Social Security racket in many countries.

All citizens become beneficiaries of the government at the age of 66, without taking a poverty oath and regardless of their financial status. Citizens who do not need these payments will no doubt waive them and be granted two (2) additional votes in exercising their suffrage by doing so. Retirement payments to elected officials become pay-

[37]Art. VII, Sec. 2
[38]Art. VII, Sec. 3

able at the conclusion of an honorable term of 8 or more years. Two-thirds of the salary which they received when active should be sufficient to make them independent. This liberal retirement pay removes all temptation when in office to violate their oath of office. Should they waive the retirement pay, they are entitled to two (2) additional votes in Precinct elections. Retirement payments preclude the recipient from being accredited with any seniority payments. Should a citizen, drawing a salary while serving in an official position, decide to waive fifty percent (50%) or more of his salary, he is granted two (2) additional votes.

The voters in possession of accelerated voting power, by virtue of such waivers, should be the best type possible. Their governmental service enables them to know government, and in the act of waiving their salaries or payments, they will have exhibited a brand of real patriotism which is assurance of their conscientiousness and honor as voters.

Frugality with Alpaca's funds will always be practiced and encouraged. In accordance with this policy, it is provided that those who are called upon to assist the elected officers in the conduct of elections will be paid on a per diem basis during the time they actually work. Citizens receiving indigent and infirm payments from the government will have no vote.[39]

Those offering themselves for office, or willing to accept office, are required to renounce their membership in political parties or participation in thought groups. They may declare their policies and furnish their qualifications in written form, but they will be pledged to make no promises to any person or group, except in their oath of office. They are pledged to discharge their duties and do whatever seems to them best, when the time for decision or action shall arise.[40]

---

[39]*Art. VIII, Sec. 1*
[40]*Art. VIII, Sec. 2*

The holders of office are forbidden to use their prestige and influence to raise funds from private sources for memorials or any other institutions. While they hold public office they are required to return all gifts above purely nominal value, from any person; and are forbidden to accept gifts of large value from any group of persons.[41]

---

[41]*Art. VIII, Sec. 3*

CHAPTER 13

SUFFRAGE

At last the time had come to resolve the most important question of all: whether Alpaca would have uniform or selective suffrage. All along this question had been the subject of intense and sometimes excited discussion.

During these Team conversations Sir Gerald Ripney had pointed out that precedents for selective voting power as compared with uniform suffrage had been set by nations dominated by a state religion. In such nations, said Sir Gerald, the citizen's voting power is decided by his contributions to the religious institution.

Jan Wauskoski, the aggressive and near-belligerent Polish student of government, was outspoken from the start for a graduated system of selective suffrage. Jan saw the answer to dictatorship in this system. He insisted that the usual "one man, one vote" practice drags the nation following it into demagoguery, demoralization and finally, in extreme instances, to complete abdication of power by the people with the surrender of property, liberty, even life itself, to a "boss."

Achala, listening to the heated conversation of the others and approaching his own conclusion, thought Jan's most likely convert was Antonio Da Vinci, a young Italian who brought to the Group sessions his superb heritage of vision and imagination, qualities which impressed them all. His mind had amazing scope for one so young, and his lightheartedness was a surprising contrast to the depth of his thinking. Excitable and peppery, he was sought out and enjoyed both for the quality of his conversation and for the stimulus he afforded.

Antonio saw some merit in Jan's contention and rather admired his courage in sticking to it. But like many optimists, Antonio prided himself on being able to define, then trying to achieve, the possible. He found amusement in Jan's frustration when confronted with the fixed opinions of the Team.

"Even if you are right," he needled Jan good-naturedly, "you don't have a chance!"

Jan also had an ally of sorts in Josef Holbrecht, who early had made known his advocacy of a limited form of suffrage —one which confined differentiations in voting power to situations in which one person had a greater stake than another. He held out for equal voting power on issues in which all had an equal stake, such as arrest and conviction for crime, privileges of the use of streets and highways, and the like. Jan, on the other hand, thought democracy could best be safeguarded by vesting control in those elements of society which could be trusted to espouse order over chaos, reason over selfish emotion. He foresaw potential mass envy of individual success endangering the stability of government and sought to forestall all the ultimate result of such envy — government expropriation of private property—by providing adequate controls to prevent it.

His views were largely opposed in the beginning. Members of the Group had studied and discussed many governments which ranged from unpopular to tyrannical—and their youthful idealism envisioned the one vote of each citizen as the ultimate weapon to overcome all government ills. That the common people are all too frequently unreasoning, as Wauskoski contended, they would not concede.

Bob and Betty Brown in particular opposed Jan's ideas. Both were convinced that uniform suffrage was the fundamental reason for their country's remarkable success as a living experiment.

"Our system," Bob explained, "was worked out between two great documents—the original Declaration of Independence in 1776 and the Constitution of 1787 in which our present government was set up. The Declaration stated without ifs, ands and buts that all men are created equal. The United States of America has gone on from there."

"Well," broke in Antonio, who was well read in American history, "I seem to recall that when the present United States government was launched in 1789 on the basis of that 1787 Constitution, the country had a very substantial slave population that was neither regarded as equal nor allowed to vote. That condition existed for practically seven decades. Even when the slaves were freed, there was no equality in voting power; and, judging from the rumblings from your country, the situation still exists."

"Yes," Jan broke in. "And you have many others ineligible to vote, minors, non-citizens not yet naturalized, those who have forfeited citizenship rights, others disqualified by state laws. Also, until very recently you had compulsory poll tax in some states, and the non-payers could not vote. Is this what you call uniform suffrage?"

Bob was unruffled. "What you say is true. But the inequities in our system are gradually being eliminated. We don't say our way is perfect. But it works, and we're making it better all the time."

"In most respects, yes," broke in Sir Gerald, who usually remained aloof from argument but often had a pertinent quote from history. "But way back in 1857 Lord Macaulay read your constitution and said your country would degenerate 'as soon as the people learn they can vote themselves largess from the public treasury by electing unscrupulous politicians.' Isn't that what's happening?"

"Of course not!" Betty said indignantly. But Achala noted that both she and Bob looked thoughtful.

All this pro and con talk had the blessing of Achala, who could see considerable room for argument. He contrived opportunities for both advocates and critics of uniform suffrage to explain their views to as many of the Team as practical. He was seeking facts with which to formulate truth, rather than a middle-of-the-road solution. Compromisers, in his view, lacked the courage of their convictions. He welcomed the hard line with no punches pulled. He saw no place for appeasers in the planning for his homeland.

Jan, wooing Antonio as a potential convert to his view, played on the latter's very dim view of the United Nations. Since the organization of this tribunal dedicated to freedom from fear and oppression, Antonio pointed out to anyone who would listen, fifty million souls per year have been lost to the slave world to be ruled by communist dictators, with the rate still going up.

"The free world," Antonio would say, "is lately losing at the rate of 80,000 people per hour for a 40-hour week."

Jan struck a telling blow for selective suffrage by casually reminding Antonio of the parallel in the UN's equality voting system. A tiny new nation, even though it may be composed of ignorant savages and cannibals incapable of governing themselves, has equal vote with all other UN members, even on propositions affecting the largest and most enlightened nations. A bloc of such small nations, representing much less than 10 per cent of the world's population, can outvote all the others. Only the veto, retained by a few of the original large members, intervenes to prevent chaos; and the veto carries no guarantee of wise usage.

Achala could see that Antonio's conviction was shaken by Jan's description of the UN system of suffrage, which was probably formulated by Alger Hiss.

The time came when a final decision had to be made. All members were present and alertly interested as Achala opened the discussion.

"One important matter you may not have considered," he began, "is that we are not dealing in theory. We are dealing with Alpaca, and Alpaca differs greatly from any of the countries with which you are familiar. Ours is an agricultural country, without the benefit to education that industry brings. We don't have a great number of people of approximately the same educational level as do your countries. Alpaca has a very few who are well educated and many who have no education whatever.

"The plan we submit will have to be approved by the nation as a whole. But first it will have to be read to all those unable to read it for themselves, and explained to all who cannot understand it. We are dependent on the educated few to instruct the masses. How can we persuade the upper classes to help us build a Republic such as our government if they are to be mere peons in it? And how can we expect the masses to exercise their citizenship intelligently if they are dependent on others for their understanding? Where there is uniform suffrage, one vote per person, the masses run the government. Well and good—if they can! But in actuality, the masses have often proved they are incapable. I fear they would prove so in Alpaca. We cannot be sure they will always take their advice from public-spirited citizens.

"I believe Jan is right," Achala continued firmly. "Uniform suffrage, for Alpaca, is the road to dictatorship. Graduated suffrage is the alternative to the indispensable man and a dictatorship."

"But this in itself creates a ruling class!" some objected.

"There is necessarily a ruling class in *any* government," Achala replied. "But the graduated voting system, which gives greater voting power to those who make the greatest contribution to their country, produces a responsible, nation-minded ruling class instead of one that can be easily corrupted."

"Until the radio inflicted the airways clown on us as a political oracle," Sir Gerald remarked, "there was a political ruling class in all self-governing countries. This was the class of the readers—people who kept themselves well informed, so much so that their advice was sought and often followed by those who were less enlightened, sufficiently to decide any close election. The employer, the shopkeeper, the preacher, the teacher, and the doctor had equal voting power in theory, but in actuality they controlled the choice of enough additional voters to bring about a higher order of political intelligence than prevails in the radio and TV age, when people no longer seek their advice."

"Which means," Achala added, "that the graduated system of suffrage is better. It perpetuates the voting power of those who are currently contributing the greatest amount to the welfare of their country, rather than making it possible for one selfish group or one individual to stay in power. I'm not saying that ruling classes can't be unsatisfactory. They usually are. But that's no reason for surrendering power to the least informed in despair of finding any better ruling group.

"Control by a class selected solely on the basis of service to the nation will unquestionably produce a superior political system. Besides, this plan can be adopted only with the consent of the people themselves. They can, if they wish, use the uniform suffrage system. But I know my people, and I think they will choose to honor their leading citizens with greater voting power and will have greater confidence in their government, knowing it is in the hands of those who have the nation's welfare at heart."

Even Bob and Betty were now swinging over to the idea of selective suffrage. "After our last discussion," Betty confessed, "we remembered that there are elections where only the property owners vote on bond issues, since they are the ones who would be called on to pay off the bonds."

"Graduated suffrage makes sense," Bob added. "A citizen's sense of responsibility rises in direct ratio to his contribution. I know from my own experience that if he has a direct stake in government and its spending, it gives him an alertness and caution in the exercise of his citizenship that you just don't find in the non-taxpayer or the very small taxpayer. The more taxes I pay, the less I like the government to waste it in handouts. What you're doing in Alpaca is vesting such decisions in the hands of those who *give* to the government rather than those interested only in what they can get from the treasury."

"That's the way any efficient corporation operates," commented Emil. "The larger the stockholder, the greater his voting power. If those with a single share of stock got control, they would bankrupt the corporation just voting themselves dividends."

Achala looked about the room. Agreement was complete. Now they had only to decide who would sit in judgment on relative voting power and on what basis additional votes would be awarded. The Group concluded that this decision as well as all others relative to voting, would be vested in the efficient and informed elected Precinct Board of Registrars already decided on.

The citizen claiming additional voting power must submit proof to the board of his contributions to the country that entitle him to an extra vote or votes. Such records are kept confidential. On the basis of information submitted and the board's findings, the board announces the number of votes to which each precinct citizen is entitled. The total of this vote constitutes the collective vote of the precinct.[42]

Under the graduated voting system, voting age is attained at 18, with no maximum age limit. Each citizen from 18 to 22 is entitled to one vote; all others to two. But the men and women who add substantially to the welfare of Alpaca have additional votes determined by the extent of their social contribution. These bonus votes are awarded in direct ratio

---

[42]*Art. IX*

to the individual's contribution to the nation. The vote of responsible citizens is thus sure to outweigh the vote of any irresponsible element which might be subject to manipulation and corruption by demagogic politicians, and self-government rests upon a secure foundation.

Premium votes are awarded as follows:

1. PAYMENT OF TAXES: Those citizens ranking among the first 25% of the direct national taxpayers of Alpaca for the previous year earn two additional votes; those in the second 25%, one additional vote.

2. SCHOLASTIC ACHIEVEMENT: Those ranking in the highest 25% of grade school, high school or college graduating class, based on a full year's attendance, earn one additional vote during the eight years following their last such scholastic achievement.

3. WAIVER OF GOVERNMENT PAYMENTS: Those waiving government retirement or seniority payments earn two additional votes; those waiving 50% or more of their government salaries are granted one additional vote. In addition, those waiving their previous year's total per diem payments are given one additional vote, provided the amount waived equals more than 10% of the average annual national salary for similar services or work.

4. VOLUNTARY PAYMENT OF POLL TAX: Citizens voluntarily paying a poll tax equal to ½ of 1% of the average annual national salary earn one additional vote.

The Group was enthusiastic in its thinking that the bonus votes would generally be used to better the quality of government. The extent of the bonus vote and its impact on elections created a statistical field day for those who tried to satisfy themselves as to the exact balance of power accruing to those paying the most taxes. Their greatest concern was the type person who would be paying the most taxes. Among the highest 25% would be the comparatively limited number who would be paying a very large part of the country's tax total. The Team reasoned that these people would be highly individualistic and would be most unlikely to see eye to eye on most issues, therefore did not constitute a hazard as far as pooling their votes was concerned. Their constructive thinking would be augmented by those in the second 25% of the taxpayers, and shaped into sound channels. This would minimize the possibility of "bloc" voting by those who paid little or no taxes.

It was recognized that it would be necessary for the government to provide a national table showing the amount of tax paid by those entitled to additional voting power. Showing the extent to which this group contributed to the general welfare would, the Group reasoned, further reduce the possibility of resentment by those who had only the normal vote.

The poll tax provision, it was agreed, was also based upon solid grounds of wisdom. Those who voluntarily pay a poll tax receive an additional vote. This mirrors a practice in very many nations where a poll tax is a requirement to qualify in voting. Also, the provision of additional votes to government employees who waive their salary or their per diem payment enriches the citizenship. Men and women who are so public-spirited that they are willing to make a personal sacrifice for the good of the nation make the finest type of voters. Certainly it is in the best interest of the nation that they cast a larger vote than those whose attitude toward the government is simply predatory. Bob and Betty recalled the example of Herbert Hoover who, while President of the USA, declined to collect his salary.

The bonus votes for scholastic achievement were prompted by Achala's reminder of the deficiency of education in his country, and the need not only to stimulate interest in learning but also to encourage greater participation in government by those youths with the most to offer.

With deep satisfaction Achala told the Group, "This is the best day's work we've done."

CHAPTER 14

PUBLIC DEBATE

The Plan Team which, ever since its inception, had included the eldest and wisest from the homeland, after a painstaking study of human experience and nearly endless comparison of different views, introduced into the Plan a radically new philosophy unknown in previous national Constitutions. They declared that debate between the principal worldwide opposing philosophies should be conducted without hysteria. Accordingly, they required that the presentation of points for either side be made in printed form in order that whatever is said will always be subject to review.[43]

To one of the basic philosophies of the world they gave the name "Liberal." Liberals generally stress human rights above property rights and strive for progress free from precedent. Liberals' belief in Government is that it is a paternal Government which will guide and care for its population. Liberal adherents are noted for their enthusiasm and are ever-blooming hardy perennials.

"Constructive" is the opposing philosophy. Constructives are staid and take pride in their stability. They are deliberative, prudent, protective and demand inviolate property rights and rule by law instead of man.

One of the most difficult duties of the Senate, as the Team contemplated it, was the requirement that it select Directors for each of the two thought groups to expound the virtues of their respective philosophies. It is difficult because they deal with indefinite and undefinable qualities. In the discharge of this function, the Senate must be wise beyond the ordinary conception of wisdom; and fair and just beyond nearly any other requirement in office. The Senate would be very guilty indeed, should it, in appointing

---

[43]*Art. VIII, Sec. 4*

Directors, put the most able exponents of one philosophy against sitting ducks of the rival philosophy, or place on the directorship of either thought group Directors who are not dedicated to the philosophy they are to represent, regardless of how good or how bad the philosophy may be in the minds of the Senators. In the discharge of this duty, the correctness of a philosophy is not within the power of the Senate to adjudge.

The Team enjoyed one of their most interesting talks in discussing the pros and cons of the two opposite philosophies of government.

During one of these discussions the subject of newspapers was raised, prompting Achala to ask, "How many daily newspapers per capita will Alpaca need in the near future?"

Hans Kyle qualified his answer:

"If it is a near-dictatorship, there will not be many daily papers needed, for there will not be much news nor much need for advertising. The outcome of primaries, elections, court decisions, and pending legislatures will be taken for granted and the government will tell the populace what they can and cannot buy. In the U.S.A., there is one daily per 100,000 people; in Czechoslovakia, one paper for 700,000; in Rumania, one each 1,400,000; and in the Soviet Union, one for each 4,700,000 people. As for smaller countries, when Castro took over Cuba the number of dailies dropped from 55 to 5 dailies. China is said to have a daily for each 85,000,000 people."

Achala was hoping for a republic with a high state of literacy. People who hope to govern themselves must be informed, and reliable newspaper coverage would afford them a high state of enlightenment when both the government and the people encouraged the communications media to be factual in news and fair in editorial policy. Unless Alpaca evades dictatorship, Achala thought, newsmen of the future would have dim prospects in his homeland.

Hans Kyle's ready information on the subject impressed Achala.

Members of the Team were certain that they had provided for one of the most important precepts for maintaining national harmony, in allowing property outlets for open discussions of both the Liberal and the Constructive points of view. The members of the Team mentioned various collapsed governments of the past which might have continued to function had such a provision been made. It should have been obvious to government leaders that attempts to choke off the presentation of the opposite philosophy could only lead the populace to attribute superior qualities to that philosophy which in fact it did not have. Overemphasis on either of the philosophies could be avoided, suggested Emil, by taking the discussion out of the realm of mass propaganda, where so much mischief has been done in the past. Consequently, the following plan was worked out.

The Constitution, as drafted, deplores the sacrifice of principles in order to attain a middle-of-the-road policy. Alpaca requires printed news media, published within its national boundaries, to make available a minimum of two per cent (2%) of printed space for the use of the authorized writing staffs for each of these thought groups. The chairman of the Senate appoints a committee of five (5) Senators to name five outstanding and capable advocates of the Liberal philosophy, and a Committee of five (5) Senators to name five outstanding advocates of the Constructive philosophy, to present their arguments to the public, printed daily. Freedom of the Press is guaranteed all citizens as well as the Right of Petition to government or its officials. Freedom of Speech is guaranteed but safeguarded under Section 4(b). Discussion of government affairs and persons is confined to printed media, precluded from radio, TV and the theater, and may not be voiced or pictured in public meetings which have an attendance of more than 700 persons. The purpose of this limitation is to prevent the illiterate or thoughtless from being aroused en masse to impulsively overcome soundly considered, responsible views expressed by the printed word. It was conceded by several of the Team that this would be a very unusual arrangement, but Achala reminded the others that some untried and unusual procedures were in order, inasmuch as the free world had lost a third of its population to the domination of dictators. It was conceded by all that this unusual presentation of the two different thought groups should be presented in printed form and the Alpaca Constitution should so provide. One member of the Team noted that a will and testament is valid only if in writing, in many countries.

The Team devoted much thought and many discussions to the necessity of avoiding "hate" propaganda in political news or anywhere else. They were in full agreement that any kind of hate was not only insidious in itself but was a waste of time as well.

"Hate is akin to oppression," Bob Brown summed up the general feeling. "Let's leave hate to the enemies of freedom."

Pertaining to non-governmental affairs, Freedom of speech in the press and in other communications media, and entertainment in the theater, by radio, cinema, or TV, is guaranteed to all citizens of Alpaca; and the Senate is instructed to enact legislation to implement the maintenance of these freedoms by curbing monopoly of ownership, management, and dissemination of propaganda wherein one race or creed can assail other races or creeds, or one class assail another class. Provisions are made for encouragement of worship, while government-supported religion and religious tests for the holding of office are prohibited. Witnesses shall not be required to testify against themselves; no person can be deprived of life, liberty, or property without due process of law. A further provision is included which will be regarded as unusual in the face of recent treaties entered into between civilized nations: that any accused person in its military service may be tried in the military or civil courts of Alpaca but never in the military or civil courts of any foreign land. Every citizen would enjoy the right to a speedy, public and impartial trial with the assistance of counsel for defense of the accused; and the provision was included that no one is to be twice put in jeopardy for the same offense. Security would be assured against unreasonable searches and seizures—century-old rights which are gradually being undermined in some countries. *Habeas Corpus* in Alpaca is not simply two high-sounding words, but a human right never in any case subject to suspension.[44]

Provision is made that all bodies and committees shall perfect their own organizations in the most practical manner except as otherwise provided.[45]

Achala, Mara and their friends, in order to avoid the inequities inherent in Civil Service organizations, decided to launch an experiment that will be decried by many as governmental aid leading to government control of education. It was provided that the government may maintain students in high school and college who will be particularly trained for service in government. Students who have been thus favored will enjoy no priorities over non-graduates in appointments to public jobs, where the merit system must always prevail.[46]

At last the day arrived when the long task of creating the new proposed Constitution was completed. The thinking people of Alpaca had been following Achala's and Mara's

[44]*Art. VIII, Sec. 4*
[45]*Art. VIII, Sec. 5*
[46]*Art. VIII, Sec. 6*

final work with mounting interest and excitement. As the new provisions, one by one, had been sent to the correspondents in Alpaca, they had been greeted with increasing enthusiasm and widespread discussion. The political atmosphere was prepared for the final document. When it was sent to Alpaca in complete form, the public began a debate which soon swept the nation. A few days later came the formal invitation to Achala and Mara to return home. It was signed by some of the most important names in Alpaca.

Their homecoming, joyous as it was to the voluntary exiles, was also an occasion of deep seriousness. The Team knew that the most critical time had now come. They had written a Constitution. It seemed to be acceptable to almost all the key people of the nation. But the country was unsettled by political turmoil. "The Man's" unsteady hands were still desperately clutching the levers of power. Could the Constitution become a reality?

As it turned out, any opposition which might have defeated their purpose quickly melted away. Public opinion was so overwhelmingly in favor of the fundamental change proposed by the Constitution that "The Man" could not hold out against it. Tired and exhausted by the years of his disastrous rule, he dropped the helm. The friends of Achala and Mara were ready to pick it up.

Achala had not known what to expect from the Alpacan young people who had formerly been his merry companions in all sorts of recreation. Would they share the serious ideals which now governed his life, and Mara's?

He need not have doubted them, for they, within their limited sphere, had been observing, thinking, maturing. Far removed from centers of sophistication, they had not been corrupted by "new," brain-distorting tactics. With very few exceptions, they took pride in Achala's attainments and rallied to his support. As for Mara, she was received by them as an uncrowned queen whose word was law. This enthusiastic cooperation from the younger set carried considerable influence and augured well for the nation's future.

Achala was tremendously popular, and with the Alpacan tendency to idolize their leaders many began to look upon him as a near Messiah.

He was implored by many to become the head of the provisional government. Some who thought more impetuously declared that he should be made the ruler of Alpaca without waiting for any due process in the working of the Constitution. Achala promptly rejected both ideas. He firmly and repeatedly stated that he had worked to plan a government for Alpaca and not a government for himself.

Again and again he stated that his greatest pride and sense of accomplishment would be in being a plain and ordinary citizen of the new Alpaca and in experiencing at first hand the anxieties, trials, and tribulations, as well as the benefits, that the Constitution had brought to the lives of average citizens. It was difficult for him to convince the people of Alpaca that this was his wish and desire, but there were so many who knew of his sincerity and the sincerity of the Achalas before him that his attitude was finally accepted. It heightened the respect in which he was held and warmed his place in the hearts of his fellow countrymen.

CHAPTER 15

ACCEPTANCE

"Mara dearest, are you glad we're back in Alpaca?" her husband asked one evening, as they found themselves alone for awhile in the patio of their wisteria-shaded home in the capital city. With the mounting political excitement, such moments of detachment were rare.

She, humming a fragment from *Faust,* was arranging a long low table with baskets of scarlet hibiscus, and placing silver containers for the aromatic fruits and juices which were a product of the Hani estates and with which the families regaled their guests. Breaking off a blossoming sprig to twist in her hair, she replied lightly:

"Yes, yes, it is wonderful here—the people are so cooperative, and fine prospects for our fondest hopes about to be realized."

"That's not quite what I meant, my precious one." Drawing her gently down to a garden seat beside him, he stroked her shining hair, and tenderly touched her cheek that was like a magnolia petal. "What matters to me is, are you happy in this environment, far from the glamour of music and theater? Does our dull life in Alpaca compensate for what you have forfeited?"

With a little rippling laugh, Mara looked at him, her luminous eyes so eloquent that words were scarcely needed. She said softly:

"Achala, my darling, don't be obtuse. Just think what you have given me instead of glamour. Most of all, your love. Your concentrated love and devotion."

"But is that enough, my diva?" he implored, out of the depths of his love and uncertainty. "After all, you have had the topmost connoisseurs of music at your feet. You were equipped to conquer the operatic world."

"And then you came along," she teased, tracing the curve of his brows with her fingers and smiling into his steadfast gaze. "You made me lose my sense of direction and brought me off on this long detour."

He still was self-reproachful. "My love for you, Mara, transcends even my love for our homeland and all our plans for its freedom. I'm not sure that it can offset your great personal sacrifice. It tortures me to think that your loss may exceed your gain. Do you long to return to Europe and resume your promising career? Does not your talent constitute an obligation to the world of art?"

"Now aren't you the foolish one," she scolded, "to sit here all solemn and brooding, counting losses, not gains? Unless," and a sudden anxiety showed in her expressive face, "unless my active participation in your work does somehow interfere with the Plan for realizing your ideas in government." Her hands fell in her lap, clasped in uneasy gesture, and her mobile face was questioning. He said helplessly:

"You interfere? What a fantastic thought. You sustain me, you give me impetus, without you I should be fractional, incomplete—" He paused, unable to find words for his emotion.

"I just thought, because the women of our country are customarily restrained, seldom emerging from the background, except socially—" Mara left her sentence unfinished, trying to think through her perplexity.

"All the more reason they need an example, learn to come out from hiding and help men to solve the problems which vitally affect us all," he responded, but rather absently, for his attention was centered on Mara as an individual, not as an exemplar. "You are my very life, and yet I would give you up rather than mar your innate self, run the risk of trimming it to fit my own."

"On the contrary," she took him up quickly, "the realness

of your love fulfills my life and self. Remember, I told you I was tired of the tinsel substitute which theater provides. Remember, I have loved you since I met you on the boat, and in my dreams before that time. Loved by you, Achala, my independent career is nothing, for I have everything."

"What you are saying I still can hardly believe," he said wonderingly, and then with swift intensity, "I wonder if you recall what 'everything' for us encompasses. Have you forgot that thrilling night when we drove across Paris and back, in a hired cab—but it transported us to the gates of paradise?"

"And the moon was at the full, the sky cloudless, the city chained in slumber, so as not to interrupt!" she exclaimed, her face again radiant.

"Yes," he said, kissing her upturned face, "the same old moon which now rises above the saw-toothed line of cedars on yonder mountain crest. And we haven't forgot, have we? —the sound of splashing waves against the Riviera beach, that night when the world stood still, and did not move at all?"

"Or the miracle," she rejoined, "of the first sunrise we watched together—that glorious sunrise that painted the sky with all possible colors!"

"I shall never forget," he assured her. "Or the way we pelted each other with hot sand, a few hours later, when the sun burned down on the stroke of noon."

"What happiness we have shared!" she said, entering his mood completely. "And shall continue to share! How can you ever doubt my happiness in the sharing?"

"It troubles me, though"—and a shade of his disquiet returned—"that you have insisted on contributing financially to the travel expense of some of our Team."

"On that point," she spoke with firmness in her voice, "I shall not even bother to argue with you. When you contribute one Pack, I contribute ten kilo, for we are partners all the way; and if I have to sell my diamonds I shall do it gladly—though I hardly expect that will be necessary, for the Hanis have been commercially minded since the dawn of time."

He bowed his head in defeat and pressed her hands to his lips. "Who, then," he murmured, "could possibly wish for more?"

"Just one more thing, perhaps," said Mara; her voice dropped to a whisper; and he noticed that her flawless skin reflected the glow of the hibiscus in her hair. "Because there really will be more. By the time Alpacans settle down to enjoyment of their new government—" she hesitated, and he prompted:

"Yes, yes, go on."

"I must tell you that I'll be having to take some time out for our own affairs, my Achala, so that we can make our really big contribution to the welfare of our country, and to the welfare of the big wide worshipful world."

Baffled, he shook his head smiling. So often did his unpredictable young wife leave him at a loss and mystified. He inquired indulgently:

"What then, sweetheart?"

"It is going to be something," she confided, while her eyes sparkled, "that will rub against your shoulder, like this. That will tug at your sleeve, like this. That will tug at your heart. That may become your greatest happiness and pride."

He exclaimed in awe and ecstasy:

"Oh, Mara, my precious, will that be a part of your happiness?"

"Part of *our* happiness," she corrected; and fluttered away to conceal her confusion in warm welcoming of guests who just then began to arrive.

After a moment of fixed abstraction he joined her in greeting their friends, and it seemed to her sensitive perception, throughout the evening, that Achala wore a new dignity and charm which sat well upon him.

And those who assembled there that night to discuss affairs of state were refreshed and invigorated by the contact. They went away feeling a confidence, an optimism, which radiated as never before from the Achala household, which would not let them falter or fail in their concerted efforts to build a better framework for their people and for posterity.

The Plan for government designed by the Plan Team, which now included other leading families of Alpaca, had been accepted when the draft of the Constitution reached them and was analyzed. Achala and Mara were delighted to be back and glad to work endlessly in assisting to familiarize the populace with it. It continued to be discussed and studied in Alpaca for many weeks.

A carefully and well-organized group, composed of the leading citizens, made tentative agreements with four men that each of them would head one of the four branches of the government. This would be a provisional government, formed for the purpose of getting the Plan formally adopted as the Constitution of Alpaca and its functions under way.

Each of the four was chosen for his experience and aptitude in the branch of government he would head, as well as for his integrity. These four Alpacan Patriots agreed to accept the positions offered and urged upon them, and it was agreed by each, and by the group who selected them, that they would serve on a temporary basis until they could be replaced by citizens elected to the high office and that their term of service would not exceed one year. They also made a pledge that they would not accept any position in the government of Alpaca within one year of the expiration of their term in the provisional government.

The close studies of the Plan had revealed some of the great difficulties to be encountered in putting it into operation. These hurdles became increasingly apparent with the continued study of its practical application. No stampede took place in favor of the Plan, and it was such a serious undertaking, with vast and lasting consequences, that no attempt was made to rush anyone into it. Speeches, such as had been made by Hitler, Mussolini, and ancient spellbinders quickly regimenting the populace of great countries, were frowned upon and were noticeably absent, for it was recognized that when the Plan became effective they would be taboo.

With many misgivings and a multitude of best wishes from people who thought they knew what they were doing, the Achala Team Plan was ratified by the provisional government and the national leaders who had selected them, and was formally adopted as the Constitution of Alpaca on the Thirteenth day of November, 1959, a day long to be remembered. When the Plan was adopted, Achala and Mara enjoyed a special thrill to which they had long been looking forward. They had dispatched a triumphant letter with thanks for their assistance to each member of the Team.

Contemplating the beginning of the new system, Achala began to think of the future. A government permitting people to successfully govern themselves will become the most benevolent government ever known, he thought to himself. Certainly it will be the most peaceful. There will be no excuse for it to be an aggressor nation, for peoples in other lands will seek it out for fellowship, cooperation and, where practical, to share in its beneficence. There would be no desire on the part of other nations to attack it, for it would be valued more as a neutral than as a participant.

Self-government will at last be an actuality without oration, declaration, demagoguery, shouts and drum-beating.

Instead, there will be the fire of patriotism of a people who are sovereign with the confidence gained through elevating the best-fitted to the highest positions in governing themselves. Idealistic?—no, for the Ideal through simplicity becomes real.

All knew that the first few years, in fact until the second general election, would be the hardest. Qualified personnel for the new branches of government, other than the Military, were scarce. Many who had been most effective in the struggle to get the Constitution adopted might be limited in executive ability when placed in responsible positions in government. As expected, there was a painful absence of administrative experience. They knew, however, that the success of the delegate system would save them from many of the growing pains of a new government.

Alpaca is fortunate in having a built-in system for weighing and studying the qualifications of its elected officers. Selections are no longer popularity contests. Men with flashing smiles, with unctuous television or radio voices, with the ability to tell a well-turned joke, no longer are preferred candidates for election. The delegates seek conscientiously for the doer and for the citizen of solid work-horse qualities. Although frequently their choice falls upon men without experience, it invariably falls upon men of character and potentiality. They are men who can learn. Although the Constitution had provided an Investigating Committee in each branch of the Government to purge the government rolls of misfits and trouble-makers, it was surprising to all how seldom these committees were forced to act during these early weeks, which afforded the supreme test.

Alpacans were not really backward people; they had needed a spirit of confidence which in the past could not be justified in view of the instability of government. In spite of the lack of dependable government and in the absence of just laws honestly administered, Alpaca had been showing signs of industrial progress. There was no prejudice against it, since it represented a better way of doing something needed than had been known before. The rate of progress was quickened after it was learned that a new plan for government had been accepted. Investment money, long in hiding, began to make its reappearance. Prosperity and peace would go hand in hand, instead of prosperity in the form of a war boom or preparedness for war. The provisional government functioned much more smoothly and efficiently than any government Alpaca had before known, and made possible the stepping up of the date of the first general election to February 1, 1960, much earlier than had been expected.

This little country, splendid in its potential, did not attract attention from abroad, for it was a very small pawn in the world's chess game of power politics. No other nation or clique of nations needed Alpaca. Its standing under its dictators had been so poor that it was ignored, perhaps even held in contempt by the United Nations.

There was nothing about this status which displeased the best people of Alpaca. They sought not to be Point IVed! They felt that their country had before it a place in the world which could command universal respect and now they wanted only to be left alone and unmolested while they were establishing their government. They thought they knew what was right and were convinced they had something which could be made to work, and which would insure peace and the greatest freedom consistent with organized society. Their Constitution was for them. They had no thought of trying to impose it on neighbors or anyone else. They looked forward confidently to the future of Alpaca, with its Constitution in which improvements were permitted which could make the country an ultimate development of organized society, and they were firm in their conviction that society must be properly organized.

They refused to listen to pious mouthings about avoiding the compulsion of the State. Alpacans wanted to be compelled to do the just, honorable, and right thing, and they wanted desperately that others be required to do the same. Then there would be Peace! It was as simple as that!

For them, November 13, 1959 would always remain a day of days!

CHAPTER 16

THE CONSTITUTION OF ALPACA

When Achala left his homeland, he envisioned a long and lonely search for the means with which his people would govern themselves. It would never have occurred to him that such a simple thing as love of liberty could act as a magnet and draw to him not only the accomplishment he sought, but love and companionship, and deep and lasting friendships as well.

The Plan Team had neither knowledge of constitutional law nor experience in government. Their only qualification for the task they undertook was a common love of freedom so intense as to dedicate them to seek a way of freedom for a country they had only heard of and a people they had never met. They found wisdom and experience of ages available to them; but the final decisions were their own — decisions reached by their information and ideas passing through the crucible of each member's thoughts until it crystallized as the product of all their thinking. They were guided by history but not bound by it, and the Constitution they produced, tailored as it was to the needs of the Alpacan people, should insure a free and tranquil government for many years.

The Team Members learned early that idealism must be tempered with realism, and that they must require themselves and one another to think beyond what was merely "right" or "wrong." Truth and Fact were essential, but there was one overriding consideration as to whether a "truth" or a "fact" found its way into the Alpacan Constitution, and that consideration was its practical application to Alpaca and its people. The Team listened to Achala, and became convinced early that insofar as possible they must put aside their own heritages and experiences, their own ideas and prejudices. Ideally, the majority of Alpacans should have had similar educational opportunities, and developed like degrees of skills with which to contribute to the welfare of their country; but as a cold, hard reality the Members were dealing with a system not of their choosing and beyond their ability to control, a system of sharply-divided classes that could neither be ignored nor soon remedied.

There were, for example, the "landed gentry" who would be unwilling to abandon the privileges — and the responsibilities, for that matter — that they had enjoyed for ages, to engage in a democratic process which would strip them of the position they had earned and reduce them to the same voting power as the indigent. Neither would the well-educated, highly-informed few willingly forfeit their station and stand shoulder-to-shoulder with the ignorant masses. And there were the merchants whose power, their ability in trade and commerce, was also the country's power in export and import and who provided jobs for so many of those less astute or less ambitious. Success of the nation was dependent on the very few who had a great deal to offer, but it had to give equitable consideration to the very many who had so little to offer; that was the situation that had to be dealt with. The masses had to have a realistic plan to help them become a part in self-government, and the plan had to consider the fact that they were peons completely ignorant of even the meaning of governing themselves.

It was the fervent hope of the Plan Team, when they completed their work, that what they had done would not stop with Alpaca; in the many countries similarly situated, or faced with the threat of communist domination, they could watch hopefully for similar plan teams to spring up following their example. In addition to their own example of success, some Team Members knew of simple letter-writing campaigns that had thwarted communism's intricate designs and even turned back the imminence of a communist takeover such as once threatened Italy. Their thinking was of the Achalas and the Maras in the backward countries, the less stable governments of the world; what youth in 1960, however freedom-inspired, could possibly foresee the successful forays of Castro and DeGaulle? At the time the Freedom Team was creating its Plan for Alpaca, its members could not foresee Fidel Castro's chameleon-like change from a self-styled "agrarian reformer" to a dictator of a Red Cuba. They had no way of foreseeing the agitation which led minorities in the USA into demonstrating, a step-up in crime rates, then to riots and finally near-insurrection. These activities would not have been tolerated anywhere in the world a short time prior to their incidence, and certainly were not to be expected in the most stable of countries. Nor could Team Members anticipate that the United States and some other democracies would begin offering and paying a premium for movements so far to the left that they could be called communistic or socialistic, or at least atheistic.

CONSTITUTION OF ALPACA

PREAMBLE

We, the people of Alpaca, yearning to achieve a just, stable and lasting form of government and to assure tranquility and peace to ourselves and our posterity, do hereby ordain and establish this the Constitution of Alpaca.

ARTICLE I.

SECTION 1. An informed and responsible electorate being basic to lasting government, all citizens of Alpaca, male or female, eighteen (18) years of age or older at the time of an election shall without educational, mental or other tests have the right to vote.

Only citizens age twenty-two (22) years or older, except in the Military, shall hold positions, namely offices, posts, or as delegates, in the Government of Alpaca. Members of the military age eighteen (18) years or older may serve as delegates and hold other positions in the Military branch of government, but in no other position. "Term," as used in this Constitution, unless otherwise provided when used and except the initial four (4) and eight (8) year terms required to establish the twelve (12) year term pattern, shall mean a continuous tenure in position of twelve (12) years with ineligibility to serve in the same capacity beyond twelve (12) years until one (1) year shall have elapsed. In initial elections and nominations, those named to the four (4) year, eight (8) year and twelve (12) year terms must be designated. Occupancy of or termination of any position shall not constitute ineligibility for acceptance of service in any other position. Ineligibility to again be chosen for service in the same capacity without the lapse of one (1) year makes rotation a reality. Proper rotation in position stimulates the highest efficiency and provides the most economical administration of government.

Service to fill vacancies and unexpired terms of seven (7) years or less does not invoke ineligibility. Any citizen convicted of participating in any subterfuge or plan to defeat this ineligibilty clause shall never thereafter vote or serve in a government position.

SECTION 2. The Provinces of Alpaca shall be divided into voting Precincts. Each Precinct shall be formed to comprise as nearly as practicable two thousand (2,000) potential voters. If any Precinct exceeds three thousand (3,000) potential voters a committee chosen by the highest College of legislative delegates representing the legislative district in which said Precinct is located shall in a reasonable time redistrict the Precincts to disturb the former Precinct boundaries as little as possible and yet conform as closely as practicable to the pattern of two thousand (2,000) total of potential voters per Precinct, and a remnant Precinct, if required, may comprise any lesser number of voters.

SECTION 3. The voters within a Precinct shall elect a Registration Board for that Precinct which shall consist of three (3) members each to serve one (1) term, one (1) of whom shall be elected every four (4) years. The Registration Board shall select and provide election judges and the clerical help and facilities necessary to hold elections.

Each Registration Board shall maintain a registration office at which every citizen must register prior to December 31 of each year to qualify to vote in the ensuing year. This registration is mandatory. Any citizen failing to register except through circumstances beyond his control shall forfeit the right to vote for a five (5) year period.

Precinct elections shall be held at publicized polling places each four (4) years at the month, day and hours set by the Senate and shall consist of a first election and a second election. In the first election the names appearing on the ballot shall be decided by petitions. The Registration Board, beginning six (6) months prior to each election, shall make available in convenient form petitions for registered voters of the Precinct who wish to nominate citizens for certain positions to be on the Precinct ballot of the first election. Any registered voter can appear during office hours and sign a petition showing the date of signature and their preference for one different citizen to fill each position for as many positions as are to be filled for which he elects to declare. Friends of citizens may circulate petitions of a similar nature to be dated when filed with the Precinct Registration Board on behalf of citizens who are willing to have their names appear on the ballot as candidates for specified positions for submission to the electorate. A Petitioner shall be limited to naming only one citizen for each position and only his nomination to fill a position first filed with the Registration Board shall be counted. The five (5) high named persons in petitions for each position, as well as all other persons named by five per cent (5%) of the Precinct electorate for that position, shall be printed on the ballot. After the results of the first election have been decided the names of the two (2) persons receiving the highest vote for each position shall appear on the ballot for the second election which shall be held two (2) weeks after the first election. The citizen receiving the highest vote for each position in the second election shall be certified by the Registration Board as elected. In case of a tie, the Registration Board shall name the winner. Precinct elections shall be by secret ballot, all higher elections by open ballot. All special, municipal and school elections shall be similarly conducted.

SECTION 4. In casting votes to fill offices the voters in each Precinct shall elect separate delegates for each of the three (3) main branches of government, being the Executive, Legislative and Judicial branches of government, and also for the Military, a minor branch of government. Each Pre-

cinct shall elect six (6) delegates in each of the three main
branches of government, two (2) being elected each four
(4) years to serve a term, Place Number 1 delegates to fill
necessary local or regional offices, Place Number 2 delegates
to vote for higher officials and delegates to form a College
to elect even higher officials or delegates to an even higher
College. Each Precinct shall also elect three (3) Military
branch delegates, who may or may not be in the Military,
one (1) to be elected each four (4) years for a term. All
Military delegates shall have the same duties and act in the
combined capacity of the Place Number 1 and Place Number
2 delegates in the three (3) main branches of government.
Delegates shall always cast a vote equal to the value of the
total registered voting power of the Precinct or area they
represent.

SECTION 5. The Precinct delegates for each branch of
government shall meet and vote with delegates of their
branch of government from other contiguous Precincts authorized by the Senate to comprise a "College." A College shall
not exceed three hundred (300) delegates, except the highest
College shall contain from one hundred one (101) to four
hundred (400) delegates. Elections shall be held in elective
Colleges one (1) month after the delegates voting in said
elections have been chosen. The College elections shall be held
in the same manner and under the same rules as the Precinct
elections except the voting will be by open ballot until the
highest Colleges of a pyramidal system have been chosen to
fill the highest offices in Alpaca. Each College shall fill the
required offices wholly within its College district which have
not been filled at a lower level and shall elect from its number
or other citizens of the College district six (6) delegates, two
(2) to be elected each four (4) years; each to serve a term
until the highest College required in each branch of government has been elected. Each delegate may serve in the same

branch of government in any number of such positions to which he may be elected from Precinct or College. He shall not serve as a delegate while holding an elective or appointive office. Should any delegate or official be convicted of participating in any trade or exchange of support with other delegates or officials he shall be guilty of bribery, disqualified from further service in the government of Alpaca and liable for all penalties for bribery.

SECTION 6. Should twenty per cent (20%) of the Precinct electorate petition the Precinct Registration Board in a manner similar to the naming of citizens to appear on the ballot by petition asking that the Precinct electorate vote directly for citizens to fill the offices essential within the Precinct, the Registration Board shall call a special election one (1) year prior to the next general election to vote upon petitioners' request. If a two-thirds (⅔ds) majority of the Precinct electorate voting in the special election approves this change in the Precinct elective procedure, thereafter the citizens to fill all positions within the Precinct shall be elected by a direct vote until such time as twenty per cent (20%) of the Precinct electorate petitions the Registration Board for a return to the delegate system originally provided in the Constitution and in a special election called by the Registration Board vote by a majority for restoration of the original delegate system.

SECTION 7. Delegates to the highest College in each branch of government shall elect nine (9) members of a Vacancy Committee to serve their branch of government, three (3) members to be elected each four (4) years for a term. Each Vacancy Committee shall by majority vote fill any vacancy occurring in any office within their branch for a vacancy term until the next general election, at which time the office will be filled by balloting for the remainder of the unexpired term, and shall in the same manner fill vacancies occurring in their own committee.

ARTICLE II.

SECTION 1. The legislative power of Alpaca shall be vested solely in a Senate and Legislative Veto Board.

SECTION 2. Alpaca shall be divided into forty (40) legislative districts, each representing as nearly as practicable one-fortieth (1/40th) of the national population. A legislative district need not be confined within the borders of a province. Each legislative district shall be represented by three (3) Senators, each age twenty-eight (28) years or older, one (1) Senator to be elected every four (4) years for a 12-year term, except that in the first election, one shall be elected to a 4-year term, one to an 8-year term and one to a 12-year term. A Senator need not be a resident of the district which he represents, but during his Senate term shall not represent any other district or area in the Senate or serve in any other position. In voting in the Senate, each Senator shall cast a vote equal to the total registered voting power of his district. The Senate shall elect from its number a Chairman, a First Vice-Chairman and a Second Vice-Chairman, each for a two (2) year period, the Chairman being ineligible to further serve as Chairman until the lapse of one (1) year. The Chairman of the Senate shall appoint Presiding Officers and Parliamentarians, from among experienced persons, age seventy (70) years or less, who are not members of the Senate, and shall appoint other operating personnel. The Senate shall at all times keep the Senate Chairmanship filled: and should a vacancy occur without any Vice-Chairman to succeed to the position, then the Chairman of the Legislative Veto Board shall call the Senate in special session. Redistricting of Legislative districts when needed shall be made by a committee appointed by the Senate.

SECTION 3. The highest College of legislative delegates shall elect a Legislative Veto Board of three (3) members, each age thirty-six (36) or older, one (1) to be elected each four (4) years for a term. The Chairman of the Senate shall appoint one (1) of these three (3) as Chairman and one (1) as First Assistant Chairman, and the chairmanship shall rotate each year. The Legislative Veto Board shall continuously advise with the Senate Budget Staff and other Budget Staffs. By a two-thirds vote, the Legislative Veto Board may veto any law passed by the Senate, in which event, the Senate can by a two-thirds (⅔ds) vote, re-enact the law over their veto.

SECTION 4. All legislation expires at the end of twelve (12) years after its enactment unless it be re-enacted by the Senate thirty (30) or more days before its expiration. The re-enactment unchanged of expiring legislation shall not be subject to veto.

SECTION 5. The Senate shall establish an equitable and uniform system of taxation. The combined total of all taxes, national, school, municipal or special district, except head tax and occupancy tax provided in Article II, Section 10 and Section 12, to prevent confiscation, shall be contained within the percentage of valuation as follows:

1. Annual Property Tax — fixed rate between ¾ of 1% and 1¼%
2. Import Tax — variable rate between 0% and 100%, depending on article
3. Export Tax — variable rate between 0% and 50%, depending on article
4. Severance Tax on Natural Resources — variable rate between 0% to 30%, depending on article
5. Gift Tax — graduated rate from 0% to 15%
6. Inheritance Tax — graduated from 0% to 25%
7. Production or Manufacturing Tax — a fixed rate on each article

      (1) On luxury items, including alcoholic beverages and tobacco — fixed rate between 0% and 100%

      (2) On necessity items — fixed rate between 0% and 4%

8. Income Tax — graduated rate from 0% to 25%

9. Sales Tax — a fixed rate on each article

      (1) On luxury items, including alcoholic beverages and tobacco — fixed rate between 0% and 100%

      (2) On necessity items — fixed rate between 0% and 4%

10. Franchise Tax — fixed rate of 0% to 2% of volume of business

Tax exemption shall not be permitted on any property owned or used by the government, nor on property, resources or income used in philanthropies of any nature, however worthy, except solely for advancing medical science, care of the sick, and public enlightenment to promote personal initiative and individual liberty.

Contributions by individuals to Alpacan religious institutions or contributions made through the religious institutions to programs supported partly or entirely by religious organizations and engaged only in advancing medical science, caring for the sick, or promoting personal initiative or any combination thereof, would be deductible limited to 20 per cent of the taxpayer's income for the year.

Taxpayers in a position to lose bonus votes by being dropped into a lower tax bracket through deductions would be so dropped unless they indicated to the contrary on filing their income reports. An organization professing adherence to a religion would be considered a religious institution by the Alpacan government only if the religion espoused by the persons comprising the religious organization acknowledges the existence of a Supreme Being. Assessments shall not be made against taxpayers of certain classes during the time the cost of collection from them would exceed fifty per cent (50%) of the revenue to be collected. Only such taxes shall be imposed in the order above recited, in the percentage deemed proper within the percentage limitation, as are essential to finance the government. Taxes shall be assessed to maintain the financial stability of the government; but the power to tax shall never be used as a power to destroy, promote philosophic objectives, or transform society in any manner except to discourage the use or consumption of harmful substances. In computing the tax on the production and sale of irreplaceable natural resources, including timber, and income therefrom, the Senate shall fix an allowance for the depletion of capital value of these resources. There shall be no payroll tax of any character whatever, and no withholding from payrolls shall be made except for voluntary health and life insurance and for income tax when legalized. Taxes shall not be assessed nor tax money spent except for purposes authorized by this Constitution.

SECTION 6. The Senate shall enact legislation for the establishment of a postal system, post offices and post roads to be operated by the Government, or if more efficient and economical by contract with privately owned companies; the arrest of persons for crime, rules of criminal procedure and punishment; the Standard of Weights and Measures, and regulating commerce with foreign nations. The Senate shall appropriate adequate funds for maintenance of the Military Branch after advising with the Commander in Chief and the National Policy Committee; and shall maintain a budget staff to recommend the levying of taxes and appropriations constituting national budgets and to confer with any budget staffs maintained by the Executive or Military Branches.

SECTION 7. The Senate shall enact legislation providing for the coinage of money, the issuance of currencies and other governmental securities, the unit value Pack, based on and redeemable in ten (10) kilograms of wheat or rice of standard grade, whichever is of lesser value, or quantities equal in value of other available commodities, or redeemable in any subsequent issue of Pack at their comparative commodity values. The Senate may revalue the commodity value of the Pack when necessary, but not more often than three (3) years from the last revaluation, but such revaluation shall not change the commodity values of previously issued Pack. The Government shall make available within Alpaca designated redemption points convenient to the public but may require twenty (20) days' notice for distribution of commodities. The Cent shall be 1/100th of the Pack in its subdivision and the Kilo 1/10th. The Pack and the multiples thereof shall be issued in currency and its 1/100th, 1/20th, 1/10th and 1/4th subdivisions shall be in coin which is redeemable in Pack of any issue but not redeemable in commodities.

SECTION 8. The Senate shall enact laws regulating the admission of aliens into Alpaca under such terms, conditions and durations as it may deem proper, together with rules governing the naturalization of self-supporting aliens who lawfully reside in Alpaca. Continued allegiance of any naturalized Alpaca citizen to a foreign country being established by judicial decree shall result in the revocation of Alpaca citizenship and prompt deportation of such person. If such allegiance to a foreign country includes treason, such person shall first be tried for such treason. All persons born or naturalized in Alpaca and maintaining active allegiance and subject to the jurisdiction thereof are citizens of Alpaca.

SECTION 9. The Senate may enact laws applicable only to certain local areas. Upon receiving a petition of twenty per cent (20%) of Precinct legislative delegates representing any area seeking a national law applicable to that area only, the Senate shall appoint a committee to hold hearings and conduct investigations as to the need for such special legislation; this committee need not include any member of the Senate and shall report to the Senate's general committee for localized laws, and the Senate may enact a national law applicable to any particular area within Alpaca, effective after a majority vote of acceptance by the Precinct legislative delegates representing said area.

SECTION 10. School Legislation shall be local laws enacted in the school district or other school divisions conforming to the Constitution. School elections shall be conducted by the Precinct Registration Board of Precincts wholly or partly within the school district with only qualified citizens residing within the area voting. Only school elections held at the same time as national elections shall be conducted at the expense of Alpaca. Taxes necessary to maintain schools shall be assessed on parents or guardians for each of their children age five (5) to seventeen (17) years at a fixed rate of ten (10) to forty (40) Pack per child within the school district; and a head tax assessed on each other adult person residing within the school district at a fixed rate of two (2) to six (6) Pack; and taxes assessed on the same but not fully used sources of tax authorized subject to the limitations set out in the Constitution.

SECTION 11. The Government shall require that children from six (6) through fourteen (14) years of age whose health permits attend a qualified school or be otherwise adequately tutored.

Children, three and four years old, who, in kindergarten pass examinations disclosing that they are qualified to enter grades with children above five years of age, may be accepted in higher grades for which they qualify if their parents desire.

The Government shall provide boarding and day school facilities, where needed, for the tutelage of the mentally inadequate.

Parents and guardians shall be responsible for each child's attendance or instruction. Those directly concerned shall be in charge of policies, administration, control and the raising of funds, but the Government shall require that the annual minimum salary for all teachers and instructors in the educational field shall be thirty percent (30%) or more greater than the average highest pay for the highest paid ten percent (10%) of unskilled hourly or per diem wage earners in the area.

SECTION 12. Charters, bylaws and laws to govern municipalities may be enacted by voters in the areas affected and shall apply only to the municipality wherein enacted but must conform to the Constitution and laws of Alpaca. Municipal elections shall be conducted by the Precinct Registration Boards of Precincts wholly or partly within the municipality with only those voting who reside within the municipality at times designated by the municipal government. Only municipal elections held at the same time as national elections shall be conducted at the expense of Alpaca. A municipal occupancy tax at a fixed rate of ten (10) to forty (40) Pack shall be assessed on each citizen age eighteen (18) years or older residing within the municipality, a franchise tax assessed at a fixed rate of 0% to 2% of value of volume, and taxes assessed on the same sources of tax authorized but not fully used by Alpaca or schools subject to the limitations set out in the Constitution.

SECTION 13. The Senate shall enact proper legislation providing for the enforcement of legal rights for wage-earning persons providing these rights from employers: disability pay for injuries; vacation with pay; to accept bonuses from employers when offered; to quit work upon notice to employer who shall honor such termination notices in order of length of service, but shall not be required to honor each day notices from more than 8% of his total staff employed at the time of receiving such notices, but all notices shall be honored within 14 days; to be paid the Wage and Hour Commission minimum wage and to accept for better workmanship or greater efficiency higher pay than the average wage for the same tasks; to recreational and entertainment facilities; to be afforded healthful working conditions; to freedom from abuse by word or deed; to be free from paying a fee to the employers or any other person or organization as a condition for securing and continuing a job. The Senate shall not enact any legislation attempting to endow a wage-earning person with a property right in employment; unemployment insurance; a right to adverse occupancy of his employer's property; or a guaranteed wage for a future period of time. The Government shall maintain employment placement offices for the free use and convenience of wage-earning persons and employers.

SECTION 14. The Government shall accredit and list all non-governmental hospitals in Alpaca and the Government shall, where needed, construct and equip hospitals, nurses' dormitories and related facilities which with existing hospitals are adequate for the hopitalization of ten percent (10%) above the average number of sick, and shall for stipulated periods place each and any hospital and its facilities, free of charge, in the custody of either a medical association, some other charitable organization or a highly efficient private profit motive organization; requiring that such hospitals and facilities be maintained and utilized to properly serve the public.

SECTION 15. The Senate shall enact legislation providing

for appropriate facilities for the care of orphans and adoption procedures and agencies for all orphans.

SECTION 16. The Government shall conduct its affairs to compete as little as possible with private industry, and shall keep at a minimum its land and real estate ownership used for national defense, parks, wild life refuges, flood control, reforestation, hospital sites, communication centers and similar ownerships absolutely essential to the function of Government, and shall be subject to suit to account to those suffering financial damage from the Government's failure to conform to these provisions.

SECTION 17. The Chairman of the Senate shall instruct the presiding officer to limit each Senator wishing to participate in the discussion of any subject before the Senate to a total of two hours, which he may use either in debate or in formal speeches.

SECTION 18. The Chairman of the Senate shall schedule action on each subject under consideration in such a way that voting shall be distributed throughout the session to prevent an accumulation of pending measures from being crowded into the closing days of a legislative session for final action, and a final vote on each measure shall be taken within ten (10) days after it is first brought to the Senate floor. A Senator may announce to the public by written word only his stand regarding any legislative measures before the Senate, but should he be found guilty of offering to pledge his support directly or indirectly to any person or any legislative measure he shall be suspended by the Legislative Investigating Committee.

SECTION 19. The Senate at the close of each session shall set a day for its next regular session and in case of emergency may be called into special session by the Chairman of the Senate or by the National Policy Committee.

SECTION 20. Bureaucracy in government makes for waste, inefficiency and a limitation of the freedom of the citizenry; therefore all agencies, bureaus, boards and commissions not specifically provided by the Constitution which may be established on an emergency basis in any branch of government shall be completely liquidated and terminated by the President within eighteen (18) months after having first been started and an annual review by an Agency Review Committee appointed by the National Policy Committee shall be made of all such entities of a permanent nature for the purpose of recommending (1) sustaining of such entity, (2) curtailment of activities, (3) reduction of personnel or (4) the complete liquidation and termination of such entity; and the findings of the Review Committee shall be promptly communicated to the President, the Chairman of the Senate and the head of the branch of government to which the entity is connected.

SECTION 21. All property, real or personal, acquired by either the husband or wife during marriage, except that which is the separate property of either, shall be deemed the community property of the husband and wife, and owned by them in equal shares. All property of a person, both real and personal, owned before marriage, and that acquired after marriage by gift, devise or descent, and the increase therefrom, shall be the separate property of that person. The Senate shall enact necessary legislation to effect and maintain such ownership.

ARTICLE III.

SECTION 1. The highest executive authority of the Nation shall be vested in a Triumvirate of three (3), each age thirty-six (36) years or older, elected by the highest College of Executive Delegates, one (1) member being elected every four (4) years for a 12-year term, except that the initial election shall be respectively for a 4-year, an 8-year and a 12-year term. The Chief of the Appointment Examining Board shall initially appoint one (1) of the Triumvirs to serve as President of the Triumvirate, one (1) to serve as First Assistant Triumvir and one (1) to serve as Second Assistant Triumvir, each for a one (1) year period, and the Presidency shall thereafter rotate each year. The two Assistant Triumvirs shall serve with full-time duties of the Triumvirate. In the event of a vacancy in the Presidency, other than through rotation, the First Assistant Triumvir shall succeed to the Presidency and the Second Assistant Triumvir shall become the First Assistant Triumvir and the Vacancy Committee shall fill the resulting vacancy. The President of the Triumvirate must be joined by one (1) of the Assistant Triumvirs or by the Chief of the Appointment Examining Board in each act or decision. Should none of these three (3) confirm the proposal of the President, these three (3), acting unanimously, are empowered to act on the subject brought to their attention by the President or on any other imperative matters of state.

SECTION 2. Qualifications of appointive officials in the Executive Branch of the Government will be passed upon by an Appointment Examining Board of nine (9) members, each age thirty (30) years or older, three (3) of whom shall be elected by the highest College of Executive Delegates every four (4) years to serve a 12-year term, except that initially three shall be elected for 4-year, three for 8-year and three for 12-year terms. The Appointment Examining Board shall organize the Board and at all times keep filled the office of Chief of the Appointment Executive Board. The findings of this Board shall be advisory, but the Board may reject any appointment made by an elected executive official. The Appointment Examining Board may establish Sub-Boards where needed, the membership of which shall be elected in the same manner as the Appointment Examining Board by the Executive Delegates authorized to fill the offices in the area in which the Sub-Board shall function; and the Sub-Board shall function under the rules prescribed for the parent Board.

SECTION 3. The President of the Executive Triumvirate may negotiate treaties with foreign powers within the framework of the Constitution, and a treaty shall become binding when ratified by the majority of a Treaty Committee composed of the Chairman of the Senate, the Chief Justice of the Supreme Court and Chief of the Appointment Examining Board of the executive department. The treaty shall become the law of the land only so far as the obligation of the Nation to carry out that particular treaty and shall not become a precedent in law.

SECTION 4. The highest College of executive delegates shall elect a Wage and Hour Commission consisting of three (3) members, each age thirty (30) years or older, one (1) of whom shall be elected each four (4) years for a 12-year term, except that the initial election shall be respectively for a 4-year, an 8-year and a 12-year term. The Wage and Hour Commission shall make a continuous study of the man hours of work needed in Alpaca and the work capacity in man hours of the people available to do the work. The purpose of the study shall be to smoothly accomplish the distribution of the volume of work needed to be done when demand for production is great within Alpaca and to prevent abnormal unemployment at all times. Semiannually, the Wage and Hour Commission shall report its findings as to the proper hours per week employment and one (1) month thereafter with the consent of a majority of the National Policy Committee, call for a prescribed number of hours as the work week and for a minimum wage for males and a minimum wage for females applying equally to all who work, with time and a half for overtime and holiday work and one and a half times the customary pay for overtime piece work. Wage earners shall not accept year, month, week, day, hour, or piece work for pay from anyone other than their regular employer if the work week is forty-four (44) hours or less, but may perform work for themselves.

SECTION 5. In the event citizens or members of the armed forces of Alpaca are forcibly and illegally detained in foreign countries, the Executive Triumvirate shall promptly enter into diplomatic negotiations to secure their immediate release. Should such diplomatic negotiations fail within thirty (30) days to secure the release and repatriation of any such persons being illegally detained, the National Policy Committee shall take whatever action is necessary to rescue and repatriate such persons.

ARTICLE IV.

SECTION 1. The judicial power of the Nation shall be vested in a Supreme Court and in such lower courts as the Supreme Court shall from time to time establish, each of which when established shall be abolished whenever there is insufficient docket to justify its continuance.

SECTION 2. A Supreme Court of nine (9) Justices each age forty (40) years or older shall be elected by the highest college of judicial delegates, three (3) Justices being elected every four (4) years for a 12-year term, except that initially three shall be elected for a 4-year, three for an 8-year and three for a 12-year term. The Supreme Court Justices shall choose one of their number to serve as Chief Justice for a two (2) year period, ineligible to further serve as Chief Justice until the lapse of one (1) year. The position of Chief Justice shall be kept filled at all times and should a vacancy occur the Court shall immediately convene, and the Justices shall re-organize the court. The Vacancy Committee shall then select a new member to bring the court up to the pre-scribed number of members. All members of the Supreme Court other than the original members must have previously served as judges in courts for a period of two (2) or more years.

SECTION 3. Judges of the lower national courts, each age thirty-six (36) years or older, elected for a two (2) year term by the judicial delegates representing their jurisdictional district, shall preside over all cases and trials within their jurisdiction, and two (2) commissioners to be associated with each judge shall be similarly elected. The judge and commissioners may render a unanimous verdict or a two-to-one verdict, and in either case their majority decision shall be the judgment of the court and if none agree, the judge alone shall render the verdict. All verdicts shall be subject to appeal.

SECTION 4. The Supreme Court shall from time to time establish labor courts to furnish wage earners and employers easy access to a labor judge of age twenty-six (26) or older, who shall be of equal stature to judges of lower national courts and elected by the same delegates electing the judges of the lower national courts. A nominal fee of 10 Pack shall be charged complainant, either employer or employee, for hearings. By appointment complainant with any witnesses he may wish to have heard may appear with or without counsel before the labor judge who, after questioning the complainant, and summoning any other parties who should be heard in the case, shall furnish complainant and defendants with a transcript of the hearing and the judge's verdict. The verdict rendered by the judge shall be subject to appeal by any party to the case to either a lower national court or to the same appellate courts to which verdicts of other lower national court judges are made, paying the usual costs of these courts.

SECTION 5. The Supreme Court shall from time to time

establish such appellate courts with such appellate jurisdiction as the Supreme Court deems necessary. The highest College of judicial delegates representing each appellate district shall elect three (3) judges; each age thirty-two (32) or older for each appellate court, one (1) judge being elected every four (4) years for a 12-year term, except that initially respectively one shall be elected for a 4-year, one for an 8-year and one for a 12-year term.

SECTION 6. The Supreme Court shall not declare any act of the Senate unconstitutional with a finding of less than seven (7) affirmative votes nor nullify executive action with less than six (6) affirmative votes. The Supreme Court shall recognize that this Constitution can be amended only as provided in Article VI and shall only construe existing laws which have been enacted by the Senate and shall not attempt to expand the meaning of existing laws in a manner which would create legislation by judicial decree; but if they find uncertainty of the legislative intent in any law, it shall be proper for the Supreme Court to request the Senate for an enactment to clarify the legislation.

ARTICLE V.

SECTION 1. The Military shall be separate from but responsible in top policy matters to the three other branches of the national government. Three (3) officers each age thirty (30) years or older to head the Military shall be elected, one to be elected each four (4) years for a 12-year term, except that initially respectively one shall be selected for a 4-year, one for an 8-year and one for a 12-year term, by the highest College of Military Delegates. The National Policy Committee shall name one (1) of the three (3) as Commander in Chief, another as First Assistant and the other as Second Assistant to the Commander in Chief, and the position of Commander in Chief shall rotate each two (2) years and the

First and Second Assistant shall at all times serve in the immediate staff of the Commander in Chief. However, the term of any of these officials may be terminated when, in the opinion of the National Policy Committee, the best interests of Alpaca justify the action. The Commander in Chief shall be responsible for the conduct of the armed forces, but as to top policy decisions shall be subordinate to a National Policy Committee composed of the President of the Triumvirate, who shall be Chairman of the National Policy Committee, the Chief Justice of the Supreme Court and the Chairman of the Legislative Veto Board. The Commander in Chief shall report to the President his proposed actions, and a majority of the National Policy Committee may withhold the Committee's sanction and the Committee shall be empowered if acting unanimously to direct the Commander in Chief to carry out any policy they consider imperative. If a decision is not reached in either manner, the issue shall then be promptly decided by the Chairman of the Senate.

SECTION 2. The National Policy Committee and the Commander in Chief acting unanimously may engage the military forces in military action against any foreign power; and acting with the consent of the Chairman of the Senate may instruct the Commander in Chief to use the military forces in suppressing rebellion and policing internal local areas if the civil authorities apply to the Commander in Chief for help in situations beyond their control. Military forces shall not be used against any citizens of Alpaca except as above provided.

SECTION 3. The Commander in Chief shall appoint the highest officer of each division of the military service and the members of his immediate staff other than the two Assistant Chiefs. Personnel for the four (4) lowest posts or ranks in each division of the military service equivalent to Corporal, Sergeant, Lieutenant and Captain will be named by their superiors, and all other military officers intermediate between these high appointive stations and low appointive ranks provided above shall be elected by the appropriate college of military delegates for the position to be filled as defined by the Senate. Excepting the Commanders in Chief, the military officers shall not be limited in term of service while able to perform their duties or upon reaching a proper uniform retirement age to be set by the Senate. In making all appointments and promotions seniority shall be considered only as one factor of merit and all appointments shall be made by merit. Those occupying elective military positions are eligible for Retirement payments.

SECTION 4. Volunteers shall be accepted into the Armed Services when needed, and in emergencies Alpaca shall have the right to conscript personnel for military service who shall receive equitable pay, and the right to conscript property for military use, the owners of which shall receive just compensation. The success of military action is dependent upon modern equipment and the personnel shall be kept at the minimum.

ARTICLE VI.

SECTION 1. Amendments to the Constitution may be submitted to the Delegate Electorate by a two-thirds (⅔ds) vote of the Senate or proposed by a majority of a Constitutional Convention of thirty-one (31) members elected by the Senate or by a unanimous vote of the National Policy Committee. Any amendment submitted by any of the three will become a part of the Constitution upon a two-thirds (⅔ds) vote of all delegates voting who have been elected in all branches of government in the Precincts. They shall be called upon to vote on the ratification of the amendment at the first general election or within two (2) years following its submission.

ARTICLE VII.

SECTION 1. The highest College of delegates in each branch of government shall elect an Investigating Committee consisting of nine (9) members each age thirty-two (32) or older, three (3) of whom shall be elected each four (4) years for a term. The duties of each of these committees shall be to investigate and hold hearings regarding the conduct of any position in such committee's branch of government. Hearings may be conducted by two (2) or more members of the committee and all information and evidence adduced at a hearing will be reported to the full committee for its action. Hearings may be open or closed. The committee by majority vote shall have the authority to call a new election at the next general election for any elected position and they may also temporarily suspend the occupant of any position. They may consider the health, habits, competency, efficiency, derelictions, temperament and integrity of the occupant who is the subject of their investigation, but in making an adverse finding they shall not publicize their reasons. An investigation by this committee shall not preclude criminal action from being taken against any person. Any investigating committee may establish a similar but inferior committee to function part or all time, if needed, to investigate minor position holders, which cases they are unable to properly investigate, but the final authority will rest in the highest investigating committee which shall be responsible for the subordinate investigating committees which it may establish.

SECTION 2. The penalty for acts of treason against the Government imposed in the Courts of Alpaca shall be imprisonment for three (3) or more years or a sentence of death.

SECTION 3. The Investigating Committee shall not deem any person being paid funds from the Government innocent until proven innocent, and shall discontinue persons from their Governmental activities upon an accusation of treasonable or illegal activities which the Investigating Committee considers substantial until such time as their innocence of such accusation has been adjudged.

ARTICLE VIII.

SECTION 1. (a) The Government shall pay each citizen upon reaching the age of sixty-six (66) a monthly installment as a Seniority payment amounting to one-half (½) of the highest average monthly earnings attained by him for any three (3) consecutive years between the ages of fifty-one (51) and sixty (60). Such payments are to be limited to an amount equivalent to the value of 400 Pack. Seniority payments to a non-salaried and not self-employed married woman shall be in the amount of one-third (⅓d) of her husband's monthly earnings limited to 300 Pack. Each citizen not in need and preferring to waive the Seniority payments due him shall be granted two (2) additional votes in recognition of a high degree of patriotic spirit.

(b) Retirement payments will be made to all elective officials who have served to honorably terminate a full term or a vacancy term of eight (8) or more years, in the amount of two-thirds (⅔ds) of the monthly salary of the office. If more than one (1) office has been held the retirement payments shall be only for the office of highest pay. The payments shall be due without regard to the status of future employment or occupation, but no seniority payment shall be made to former officials receiving retirement payments. Any elective official, after reaching the age of sixty-five (65) years, may retire, drawing full pay for the remainder of the term to which he was elected and retirement pay thereafter. Each citizen preferring to waive retirement payments when eligible shall be granted two (2) additional votes in recognition of a high degree of patriotic spirit. Each citizen occupying a salaried government position who prefers to waive payment of fifty per cent (50%) or more of his annual government salary shall be granted one (1) additional vote in recognition of his desire to lessen the cost of government. Each citizen occupying a salaried government position who prefers to waive a previous year's total per diem payments, if amounting to more than ten per cent (10%) of the average national salary for similar work shall be granted one (1) additional vote.

(c) Delegates to represent the electorate in a Precinct or College of delegates shall not be considered officials and their pay shall be considered per diem payments for time actually given to their work and not salaries. This is true of all clerical help in holding elections except the Registration Board and any other part-time and temporary helpers.

(d) Indigent and infirm citizens shall be paid by the Government a monthly sum sufficient only to cover their necessities. The Senate may provide for resident persons a payment during the time such persons are seriously sick, only so long as their sickness lasts.

SECTION 2. Persons offering themselves for office or willing to accept office shall renounce their membership and participation in any and all political parties or thought groups but may announce their opinion regarding policies and truthful and accurate records of their past training and achievements in written form only but shall not make any promises of any nature whatsoever to any person or group except to pledge to take the following oath of office: "I DO SOLEMNLY SWEAR TO UPHOLD THE CONSTITUTION OF ALPACA, EFFICIENTLY DISCHARGE MY DUTIES AND PERFORM MY OFFICIAL ACTIONS TO ACCOMPLISH WHATEVER APPEARS TO ME TO BE IN THE BEST INTERESTS OF ALPACA WHEN THE TIME

FOR DECISION OR ACTION ARRIVES."

SECTION 3. (a) The holders of offices and other governmental posts or positions shall not participate in any manner
in the raising of funds from private sources for any institution
or endeavor.

(b) Any citizen, elective or appointive, in any national,
municipal, or school position shall not accept but shall return
to the donor any individual gift in excess of a nominal value
equivalent to 5 Pack, or any gifts from different persons
comprising an aggregate value in excess of the equivalent to
100 Pack.

SECTION 4. (a) The Government of Alpaca declares that
a continuing presentation of views and information and a
constant debate between the two (2) worldwide opposing
philosophies of government is a proper and wholesome governmental activity when carried out in a manner to avoid
hysteria, prejudice and emotion in an attempt to formulate
the best possible policies for orderly government. The printed
word is subject to verification, review, analysis and evalua-
tion and reaches the better reasoning power of those who
read with understanding, therefore it provides the proper
avenue for such debate. The two (2) thought groups of
opposing philosophies may be best described as follows:

LIBERAL—Stressing privileges for the masses; progress
unhampered by tradition, humanitarianism regardless of
property rights, paternalistic government, social gains
and associated and similar objectives.

CONSTRUCTIVE—Stressing inviolate property rights,
individual initiative, the profit motive, free markets, protection against governmental monopoly and associated
and similar objectives.

Principles should not be sacrificed in order to attain a
middle-of-the-road policy but it may be from time to time

the extreme views of either thought group may not provide as salutory or sound governmental policy as a policy tempered by and leaning toward the opposing philosophy. Therefore, Alpaca shall require printed news media published therein to make available free a minimum of two per cent (2%) of space for the use of the authorized writing staff for each of these thought groups. The two (2) authorized writing staffs shall be chosen and comprised as follows:

LIBERAL—The Chairman of the Senate shall appoint a committee of five (5) Senators to name the most able, ardent and persuasive advocates of the liberal philosophy. From those named by the committee, the Chairman of the Senate shall appoint directors, who hold no governmental positions and who are willing to serve in that capacity without salary from the government, five (5) in number, one (1) to be appointed each year to serve for five (5) years. Initially, the five shall be appointed for one, two, three, four, and five-year terms. The five (5) directors so chosen shall organize their staff and prepare or cause to be prepared the printed current presentation of their philosophy.

CONSTRUCTIVE—The Chairman of the Senate shall appoint a committee of five (5) Senators to name the most able, ardent and persuasive advocates of the constructive philosophy. From those named by the committee, the Chairman of the Senate shall appoint directors, who hold no governmental positions and who are willing to serve in that capacity without salary from the government, five (5) in number, one (1) to be appointed each year to serve for five (5) years. The five (5) directors so chosen shall organize their staff and prepare or cause to be prepared the printed current presentation of their philosophy.

In addition to these officially sponsored opposing columns,

freedom of the press, including all non-libelous statements regarding affairs and policy of government and its personnel is guaranteed all citizens of Alpaca. The right to petition the government or officials shall never be infringed upon.

(b) Discussions of governmental affairs and persons are confined to printed media, precluded from radio, TV and the cinema and shall not be voiced or pictured in public meetings attended by more than 700 persons. Within these limits freedom of speech regarding any matter or person pertaining to government is guaranteed all citizens of Alpaca. Pertaining to non-governmental affairs or persons, freedoms of speech, press, communications, presentation of wholesome entertainment in theater, by radio or television are guaranteed all citizens of Alpaca and the Senate shall enact legislation to implement the maintenance of these freedoms at all times by curtailing any monopoly of ownership, management or policy and curtailing the dissemination of false propaganda, either open or subtle, wherein one race or creed assails other races or creeds or one class assails another class; and curbing all unbalanced programs tending to undermine freedom and government.

(c) Worship shall be encouraged in Alpaca but Alpaca shall never have any government-supported religion, nor shall the Senate make any law regarding the establishment of religion or prohibiting the free exercise thereof, nor shall any religious test or qualification be a prerequisite to holding elective or appointive position; nor shall any Bill of Attainder or *Ex Post Facto* law be enacted.

(d) No person shall be held to answer for a crime unless served with a formal court summons nor shall be compelled in any criminal case to be a witness against himself nor be deprived of life, liberty or property without due process of law, nor shall private property be taken for public use without just compensation. A person in the military service of Alpaca shall be tried only in the military or civil courts of Alpaca, and Alpaca shall never consent to the trial of a member of its armed forces in the military or civil courts of any foreign land.

(e) In all criminal prosecutions the accused shall enjoy the right to a speedy, public and impartial trial in the district where the crime was committed and to be informed of the nature and cause of the accusation; to be confronted with witnesses against him; to have compulsory service for obtaining witnesses in his favor; to be entitled to bail except in capital offenses and to have the assistance of Counsel for his defense; and not to be twice put in jeopardy for the same offense.

(f) The right of the people to be secure against unreasonable searches and seizures in their persons, houses, papers and effects shall not be violated, and no Warrants shall issue but upon probable cause, supported by oath or affirmation, and particularly describing the place to be searched, and the person or things to be seized.

SECTION 5. All bodies and committees shall perfect their own organization in the most practical manner except wherein otherwise provided.

SECTION 6. A branch in high schools and colleges, not to exceed 3% of the National attendance any school year, may be maintained at government expense to provide training for governmental service, but the graduates from this branch in high schools and colleges shall have no higher preference of tenure over non-graduates for governmental jobs as the letting of such jobs shall be based on merit.

ARTICLE IX.

SECTION 1. Each citizen shall be endowed with a voting power based on his age, experience, active interest and investment in government, and tax paid to the nation during his previous tax year, as he may prove to the Registration Board of his Precinct of residence, with the voting power assigned to each citizen to be graduated and cumulatively determined as follows, provided that the maximum voting power for any one citizen shall not exceed five (5) votes.

	Votes
Each citizen age 18 years or older	2
Additional votes awarded to citizens qualifying:	
a. If one of highest 25% of direct National taxpayers	2
b. If one of highest 25% to 50% of direct National taxpayers	1
c. A bonus vote for scholastic achievement, if in the highest ranking 25%, whether in grade school, high school or college graduating class based on the full year of attendance, but only for the next 8 years following the last scholastic achievement	1
d. For waiving payments from Government:	
(1) Retirement or Seniority payments	2
(2) 50% or more of government salary	1
(3) Previous year's total per diem payments if amounting to more than 10% of the average national salary for similar services or work	1
e. If Poll Tax voluntarily paid equal to ½ of 1% of the average annual national salary	1

(Note: All averages arrived at on the basis of the previous year.)

The voting power of a direct national taxpayer, at his request, shall be increased by crediting him with the pro rata part attributable to his ownership of taxes paid by any company or enterprise in which he owns stock or an interest. The citizen, who must have resided in the Precinct three (3) or more months to qualify to vote, may register each year and may make his proof of any additional votes based on his last fiscal tax year with the Registration Board within ten (10) days to one (1) year prior to each election in which he seeks to vote. A citizen residing in the Precinct for more than two (2) years shall be subject to a penalty to be prescribed by the Senate for failure to register with the Precinct Registration Board. The tax record of each voter shall be held confidential. A wife (primary, if plural) shall exercise equal voting power with her husband.

The Constitution of ALPACA is herein instituted on a basis of graduated suffrage (Art. IX, Sec. 1), but the ALPACA Senate has the power by majority vote to change from the graduated suffrage system and provide for uniform suffrage whereby each qualified voter shall have the same voting power. The ALPACA Senate shall also have the power, by majority vote, to revert to the graduated suffrage system first established in the Constitution; and the Supreme Court shall recognize such changes made in the suffrage stipulations as the law of the land.

———————◆———————

AUTHOR'S COMMENT: Where the Constitution may prove inadequate it does not require circumvention, for it provides that it can be amended with definite provisions free from ambiguity and, should the urgency be great, the amendments can be made promptly while Alpacans, without hardship, remain law-abiding citizens. A written Constitution is both better than and a safeguard against any dictatorship, even a benign one.

The ALPACA Constitution was translated from English

into Spanish and later into Arabic, November 1966. The Jesuit Order caused it to be translated into Vietnamese to make it available to the Assembly. The Vatican caused it to be translated into Russian and into Mandarin, which is understood by 700 million people. It was translated into German and French in March, 1967.

Jules Weill, prominent in the entertainment field in Hollywood, also caused the ALPACA Constitution to be translated into Mandarin and recordings of it were aired on radio stations in Southeast Asia, where it could be heard in North Vietnam and China Mainland. Among the many languages to which the ALPACA Constitution has probably been translated, it is reliably reported to have been translated into Serbo-Croatian, a language understood by 14 million in Yugoslavia, and Tagalog, understood by many in the Philippines, the Malay Peninsula and in Indonesia.

ALPACA

How much is that book in the window?
   The one that says all the smart things,

How much is that book in the window?
   I do hope to learn all it brings.

I must take a trip into romance
   And leave my poor sweetheart alone.

If he has a book he won't be lonesome
   And Alpaca will give him new tone.

I read in the papers there were robbers
   With flashlights that shine in the night,

My love needs a book to protect him,
   Alpaca will turn on the light.

I don't want a bunny or a kitty,
   I don't want a parrot that talks
     (aside—"Polly wants a cracker")

I don't want a bowl of little fishes,
   Alpaca is Jack's new bean stalks.

How much is that book in the window?
   The one which my Popsy wrote,

How much is that book in the window?
   You can buy without signing a note.
ALPACA

A parody on "How Much Is That Doggie In The Window," written and sung by Helen and Swanee Hunt when they were 10 and 9 years old.

The Alpaca Waltz

Cantabile

by Johnny Singer

SIDE PO-EMS TELL NO SWEET-ER STO-RY MAN HAS FOUND NO FIN-ER GOLD THAN THE LOVE FOR GOD AND COUN-TRY AND A LOVED-ONE HE CAN

RITARD

HOLD.

WHEN *ALPACA* was published in 1960, Johnny Singer was the very fine leader of the orchestra at the Mayflower Hotel in Washington, D. C. H. L. Hunt presented him with a copy of *ALPACA*, and he lost a night's sleep reading the romance. The next day he came to Hunt and said, "I would like to have the honor of preparing a piece of music to *ALPACA*." In the next three or four nights, his orchestra rehearsed and played "The Alpaca Waltz." After the Waltz proved to be popular with the diners and dancers, a friend of Johnny Singer supplied him some words to go with the music. These words have been changed from time to time.

HUNT'S GARAGE

PHONE 1721

Lorton, Nebraska

Oct. 28, 1957.

Mr. H.L. Hunt,
Dallas, Texas

Sir: not longago I see you listed as
the top dog (financially) and was
impressed that one with the same name
could achieve such distinction.
    What the H--- is the matter are
you slipping? I see you rated today
in the second string list. Now get
on the ball and get back in the top
bracket where you belong, us Hunts
don't recognize any second raters??

                    Sincerely
                        C. Hunt.

H. L. HUNT
1704 MAIN STREET
DALLAS 1, TEXAS

Mr. O. Hunt
Hunt's Garage
Lorton, Nebraska

Dear Mr. Hunt:

      I am replying to your letter of October 25, 1957 which
I reproduced and a copy of which I enclose. I was in Kuwait, Beirut
and London for about 6 months shortly after I received your letter.
Just before I left for the Middle East the New York Times Sunday
Magazine Section wrote me up as worth a little 'ole 2 billion and
the richest man in the world, so I was in the top bracket for a little
while, but Fortune and Life soon spoiled everything by writing me up
as 2nd to Getty.

      I used your letter and these write-ups as a financial report
in my negotiations for a fantastic concession in the Middle-East.

      I am sure that astute as you are you know that all of these
reports are stuff and nonsense. Your particular letter was one of
the few pieces of welcome mail which I have ever received as a result
of write-ups of this nature.

      In addition to the copy of your letter I enclose some LIFE
LINE material. I have been trying to help this worthy organization.

      With my very best wishes,

                  Constructively,

                  H. L. Hunt

APPRAISAL OF ALPACA

BY HEADS OF FOREIGN NATIONS

AUSTRIA

I have the honor to acknowledge receipt of your letter of November 19, 1966 and wish to thank you for sending me a copy of the new draft of the ALPACA Constitution.

CHINA

The President has read your book with much interest and he is grateful to you for sending it to him.

To place them where they can easily be reached, I have sent your book to six educational institutions and government agencies. I hope many of our friends will read it.

COLOMBIA

I acknowledge the receipt of and thank you for your letter of November 19 and the enclosed copies of the Constitution of Alpaca which you have published.

CYPRUS

We acknowledge with thanks receipt of your letter and copies of your revised draft "constitution" published in your book ALPACA in 1960.

DOMINICAN REPUBLIC

Thank you very much for sending us the enclosed brochure and material describing the constitution which you published in your book ALPACA, in 1960, and which we have found very interesting and useful.

FINLAND

Yours is a very interesting and informative accomplishment.

FRANCE

I have read with great interest the text of the Constitution which was enclosed.

You might be interested in receiving the text of the French Constitution which is enclosed. I found it to be a very valuable and interesting document.

We will keep this document in our archives and I am sure it will be used by many students of constitutional law.

HUNGARY

I will forward it to Budapest.

In the meantime allow me to send you a copy of the Hungarian constitution.

IRAN

We are always glad to receive at the Embassy of Iran any works which help to promote, as you say, the cause of freedom and thank you for bringing your publication to our attention. Should we need any further publications we will certainly contact you.

JORDAN

I wish to thank you for your letter of November 19, enclosing a copy of the 1960 Alpaca Constitution which you authored and published.

I will certainly try to look into it and will let you know my comments, if any.

LATVIA

I fully share your views that a workable constitution is a necessity in the present times. I appreciate the originality of your ideas embodied in the enclosed text. I hope that your ideas will find a following and success.

LIBERIA

Thanks for the copy of the new drafts of the constitution published in your book ALPACA in 1960.

MEXICO
It was very good of you to send me copies of the Constitution for a mythical country—Alpaca—which you have drafted having in view the problems and needs of emerging nations.

PERU
It certainly represents a tremendous amount of work on your part, and I appreciate your making it available to me.

REPUBLIC OF THE PHILIPPINES
President Ferdinand E. Marcos wrote me October 11, 1966, thanking me for ". . . the Constitution of Alpaca, A Mythical Country. Congratulations and more power to you . . ." On January 20, 1967, he wrote in part, ". . . My receipt of the Constitution of Alpaca is very timely for our Congress is scheduled to prepare some amendments on our Constitution . . ."

SOUTH AFRICA
I should like to thank you for your letter of 19th November, 1966, addressed to the Ambassador, which has been read with interest.

SPAIN
Your project is very interesting, and you were kind to send it to me.
The world is indeed fortunate that there are still men who are concerned about the forms of government and the future of all nations. May their concern always lead to better understanding and cooperation between all nations.

THAILAND
On behalf of the Ambassador who is at present on an official mission, I wish to express our thanks and ap-

preciation for the above letter and for the constitution of ALPACA. I need hardly assure you that the constitution will be studied with great interest.

REPUBLIC OF TOGO

Je vous remercie au nom de l'Ambassadeur du Togo, Docteur Robert Ajavon, pour votre aimable lettre du 19 Novembre 1966 par laquelle vous avez bien voulu nous faire parvenir quelques numéros de la "Constitution d'Alpaca".

Ce document tres intéressant a retenu toute mon attention et m'a permis de me rend're compte des valeurs morales qui ont été a la base de sa rédaction.

UGANDA

I dare to suggest that it is a good constitution which could be utilized profitably by some of the emerging nations.

URUGUAY

I have forwarded a copy of the draft to the Law School of the University of Montevideo as I am sure that their Seminar on Constitutional Law will find it most interesting.

VIETNAM

I wish to thank you very much for the Constitution of ALPACA, a Mythical Country, which you recently sent to me.

The Prime Minister, Air Vice Marshal NGUYEN-CAO-KY, has instructed me to convey his sincere thanks to you and to refer your document to our Constituent Assembly for study.

The ambassador from South Viet Nam to the U. S., Vu Van Thai, was in Dallas. I called upon him in his hotel suite and gave him copies of the Alpaca constitution in English.

He was anxious for the delegates to the Assembly and the 40 daily newspapers in South Viet Nam to be supplied with the model constitution for the people of the emerging nations.

TIME Magazine, March 24, Page 22, in a column, "South Viet Nam," stated "the delegates drafted and debated for days messages of initial greetings to the Vietnamese Army, the U. S. Army, the U.N., the people of the U.S., the people of Viet Nam. (The only reply they got was from Conservative Texas Oilman H. L. Hunt, who sent each deputy a copy of his own model rightist constitution, 'Alpaca.')"

I received messages of appreciation from some of the officials from South Viet Nam and one from President Chiang Kai-shek of Taiwan's office. President Ferdinand E. Marcos of the Philippines wrote me two or more letters of appreciation stating in one "My receipt of the Constitution of Alpaca is very timely for our Congress is scheduled to prepare some amendments on our Constitution."

During this time I wrote letters to the Editor of U. S. papers calling the public's attention to the Constituent Assembly. I suggested that everyone with views regarding the type of constitution South Viet Nam needed should convey their views to the South Vietnamese.

Life Line
FREEDOM TALK
A Daily Radio Commentary By
LIFE LINE FOUNDATION
4330 N. Central Expressway
Dallas, Texas 75206

This is LIFE LINE, *Melvin Munn from Dallas.*
NUMBER: 66-D

UN OR PEACE LEAGUE?

High Spots Opposite Asterisks

With so much talk today about the United Nations, we tend to overlook many of the events leading up to its formation. Especially are we inclined to forget its predecessor, a former international organization called the League of Nations. This world body was the product of World War I, and principally the ideas of General Smuts, Leon Bourgeois and Lord Robert Cecil.

* The chief figure in the founding of the league at the Paris Peace Conference in 1919 was President Woodrow Wilson. On January 10th of the following year, 1920, the league was officially established at Geneva, Switzerland. Despite intensive efforts, President Wilson was unable to persuade the United States Senate to confirm the league as a treaty. Primarily responsible for blocking ratification were Senators Henry Cabot Lodge and Hiram Johnson.

Twenty-six years later, in 1946, on the same date it was established, the League of Nations was dissolved. At that time Mr. H. L. Hunt of Dallas, Texas was deeply involved in helping formulate a sound, workable peace league plan. And he has subsequently contributed significant ideas on such a proposal.

In April of 1946, the League of Nations closed its work and gave its physical assets to the United Nations. But how did the successor to this world organization come into being?

*   In the fall of 1944, in the Georgetown area of the capital, the Dumbarton Oaks conference was held. It was followed, during the first week of February of the next year, by the Crimean Conference of Roosevelt, Churchill and Stalin at Yalta. There it was agreed to call a conference on April 25th. This was done; and representatives of 39 nations met in San Francisco to form the United Nations.

Meanwhile, Mr. H. L. Hunt, who had watched closely the events leading to the formation of the League of Nations and had studied its activities carefully, viewed with concern those events leading up to the San Francisco conference. He did not believe it desirable or feasible for this country to participate in a world organization. However, he realized that, in all probability, one would be formed.

Having considerable knowledge of the international Communist conspiracy and mistrusting some of President Roosevelt's close advisers and some in the State Department, he had cause for concern. Yet he was not fully aware of the philosophies of Harry Dexter White, who had been so influential at Dumbarton Oaks, or of Alger Hiss, who played such a key role at San Francisco. It is generally conceded that these two men provided the basis for the present formula for the General Assembly of the United Nations.

Hoping that some of the mistakes which might be made at San Francisco could be avoided, Mr. Hunt prepared a plan for a world organization. First writing the plan in narrative form, he next outlined it, to be placed in the hands of some of the world leaders. His plan was sent to the late Winston Churchill, Dulles and others, who later attended the gathering in San Francisco. This he did, expecting that these men would be highly influential in the preparation of a peace league.

Mr. Hunt was motivated by a sincere desire to assist in a

constructive manner in the preparation of the charter which he felt would be enacted. When the wording of the UN Charter was made public, he was deeply disappointed that his Peace League Plan had not been used.

* Just what was his plan? And why the need for any world organization? The author himself explained that nuclear developments today give more reason than heretofore for nations to be organized in a world-wide body.

With reference to the United Nations, he points out that the Soviets undoubtedly can win any vote they wish in its General Assembly. Despite their repeated threats to withdraw from the UN, he is of the opinion that the Russian communists probably will remain—since the UN serves their aims so conveniently and so well.

Mr. Hunt does point out, however, that Soviet Russia's membership in that world body serves one purpose approved by American patriots. And that is, that Russia no doubt will refuse to permit admission of Red China to the UN.

He warns, though, that if the United Nations is not reformed, affording the United States voting power commensurate with its assets and responsibilities, we should withdraw from it—if we are to survive!

In this connection, it is quite true that certain UN reforms have been suggested. From time to time thoughtful and courageous Americans have advanced proposals for changing the charter. Deeply conscious of the ineffectiveness of the UN as presently constituted, the late President Hoover proposed that a world body of free nations be organized.

* Constructive plans and suggestions notwithstanding, the propaganda machinery of the UN and its one-world advocates is so powerful that little is ever heard of these plans. And in the minds of many unthinking people, the UN has become so sacrosanct that reforms or alternate plans are automatically discouraged—sometimes cruelly attacked.

The author of the books, *Alpaca, Govern Thyselves, Why Not Speak?* and *Fabians Fight Freedom,* for many years has fought to preserve our Freedom way of life. No Johnny-come-lately on the scene, he drew up a blue print for a workable peace league during World War II. His ideas were submitted to some of the world leaders before the UN Charter was drafted. Unfortunately, Alger Hiss and others of a different philosophy were successful in drafting the accepted plan which now governs the operations of the United Nations.

The three aims of Mr. Hunt's plan were: to enforce treaties ending present wars; to prevent future wars; and to set up and maintain an Arbitration Council.

* But why a peace league? Here are his own words of explanation: "Great wars cannot be justified; the cost in loss of life, health, faith, ethics and property, is far too great. The things fought for are seldom realized by the victors. The causes are generally trivial, and the results are that nothing is satisfactorily settled."

He went on to say that "If great wars are absolutely prevented, there may be expected such an advance in civilization that gradually equity and justice will become understood, and so popularized that the working of these principles will be depended upon."

Mr. Hunt then prophesied that, "the simple exercise of them will result in adjustments taking place in national and international affairs, so that society will become workable and livable with a minimum of jealousy and strife."

He proposed that nations at war with Germany and Japan, or those that had broken relations with them, be asked to voluntarily agree as to the share of each in the control and responsibilities of the Peace League. Each nation's percentage would be determined by joint consideration of these particular factors:

The nation's contribution to repelling the forces of oppression in World Wars I and II; its population; the nation's standard of education and state of enlightenment; its record of non-aggression; a nation's wholesome commerce; its assets; and the extent and nature of its area.

He was careful to include a provision whereby additional nations, by treaty with the Peace League, might be admitted. A safeguard was written in, providing for the percentage participation to be surrendered by Peace League members in the same proportion as the participation of each.

This particular part of the proposed plan is of great importance today when more and more small, newly emerged nations are being admitted to the United Nations. It is highly significant today when the United Nations' very existence is being threatened by Russia's refusal to pay its debt to the United Nations. And it is cause for sober reflection by the American taxpayer who sees his country paying the lion's share of the operations of this constantly enlarging world body.

In an effort to police some of its own extravagant financial policies, the United Nations Advisory Committee asked for a budget ceiling. However, as is the case in most bureaucratic bodies, the call for thrift is exceedingly unpopular and generally goes unheeded. The UN has proved to be no exception. Meanwhile its fiscal problems mount with each passing hour.

* But let's turn back to the 1945 outline for a Peace League plan, as proposed by H. L. Hunt. The architect of this outline envisioned an Advisory Board, to be selected from representatives to the League. These men would arbitrate and render decisions on issues as they would arise.

Provision was made for the withdrawal of nations desiring to do so, and for their share of the operating costs to be prorated among the remaining nations.

The plan also called for the selection of seven members to

an Arbitration Council. These men would be elected by the Assembly and no more than one Council member from the same nation would serve at any one time. He foresaw the Arbitration Council attracting the world's greatest men. And he predicted that these men, while serving on the Council, would dismiss all selfish interests of the nation from which they came, if conflicting with the greatest good. The candidates offered by each nation, he concluded, would be chosen from the heads of the government, the chief justices of their courts, their greatest legislators, cabinet members, ambassadors, and representatives to the Peace League Assembly.

To these men would be entrusted the responsibility for formulating an International Code to supplant the then existing international law, the Atlantic Charter, the Moscow declaration, and all such similar rules and declarations, as outlined in this 1945 plan.

* This Council of arbitrators would, through the fairness and justice of its decisions, be a medium for their enforcement rather than an arm of enforcement of international law. And the author explained that enforcement would be dependent upon public opinion, except that the Council might request disputants to pledge that they would abide by the decision to be handed down by the Council.

Mr. Hunt saw the pronouncements, rulings and decisions of the council accorded the dignity of international law by the Peace League Assembly. Here he inserted another safe-guard. He noted that since the Assembly was primarily required to prevent war, he said the decisions of the council would not be binding upon the assembly in case that body decided that such decisions might endanger world peace, unless the assembly had agreed in advance of the decision to enforce it.

Because of the great interest in this peace league proposal, the complete outline appears as an Appendix to Mr. Hunt's latest book, *Fabians Fight Freedom*. Students of history and of political science will find this blueprint for a world body thought-provoking. For the many who deplore US continued participation in the UN as presently organized, the plan presents some challenging ideas.

The Peace League plan is also a forceful reply to the cry of the Farleft, to those who unthinkingly accuse constructives of criticizing but never offering an alternate or better solution. It merits the attention of all Freedom-loving people.

Until we meet again, remember: The Peace League plan was ignored in favor of the philosophy of Harry Dexter White at Dumbarton Oaks and Alger Hiss at San Francisco, which provided the present formula for the General Assembly of the UN.

YOUTH FREEDOM SPEAKERS

Youth Freedom Speakers, now under way, can expand worldwide at the same time they are becoming nationwide. These 15 to 23 year old speakers who are popular in delivering their 3-minute speeches to service clubs, churches, on radio and TV, are a completely natural weapon for the truth side. Every church junior choir can become a greater choir and do far more in defeating the atheistic enemies if it is represented by one or two Youth Freedom Speakers who, in addition to speaking about public affairs, can testify and "witness for Christ." If they now number 300, they can soon number 1,000; and when there are 10,000, they will begin realizing their goal of cutting the crime wave in half. When there are 50,000 Youth Freedom Speakers, we can begin bringing our soldiers back home; and when there are 100,000 throughout the world, wars may become a thing of the past and communism collapse unless it is a better system of society than individual initiative and profit motive.

The Board of Counselors of adult professional men and women who find working with youth keeps them young, can engage in the very best national and state nondenominational and nonpartisan activities.

There are 1,100,000 letter-to-the-editor writers, and any brief letter on a neglected subject can spur other writers into action. This forum is the most widely read of anything beyond the front page. In addition to stimulating discussion on the subject which is "out-managing managed news," the average copy of a paper is scanned by 3 persons. A letter appearing in a paper of 200,000 circulation will be read by 600,000 "scanners." Two percent — 12,000 — of them will probably write a letter to the forum columns they like and it will have its weight even if not published. If you would like to reach your M.C., and who wouldn't, send him a copy of the letter you have written and cause four or five friends to inscribe their name, address and telephone number under a stipulation, "We concur," and you have produced an effective petition which he and his staff will read and weigh.

FREEDOM MESSAGES

Patriots are anxious to know what they can do to preserve their liberty and the Nation's independence and sovereignty. They must not despair, and are entitled to hear good news when it comes. You need wring your hands in anguish and helplessly ask, "What can I, alone, do?" or "What can we have found the best or you originate better moves.
do?" Here are suggestions of a few things to try until you

In your day-to-day contacts, wherever you are, and whomever you are with, mention the blessings of living in Freedom. Your words may impress someone that has been heedless, and another enthusiast, or maybe 10, for Freedom will have been won.

Support patriotic organizations in your community. Encourage the American Legion, Veterans of Foreign Wars, the great auxiliaries, Boy Scouts and women's groups such as DAR and others. They are dedicated to defending Freedom and vigilant in exposing the plans and tactics of Freedom's foes. They seek no rewards but the knowledge they are helping to keep our Republic free.

Pursue the "each one teach one" idea. There are at least 2 million active patriots in America today who realize our liberties are threatened. If each of these on the average would activate just one other person to the Freedom cause every 3 months, in 6 months there would be 8 million active patriots and in a year 32 million. This formula does not ask for one active participant to win one other each day or each week, but one freedomist each 3 months. Unquestionably, any active patriot can be expected to activate another person in 3 months. Soon the spirit of liberty would overflow to foreign lands, and so long as the contests are between liberty and slavery, war might be outmoded. If there are a few who could stir none, there will be clergymen, teachers, or "good mixers" who might inspire 20 or more bringing up the average.

Never feel that working for Freedom means you must labor and suffer under a heavy burden. Freedom is a grand and joyous idea and working for it can be sheer delight. Find what you can best do for Freedom each day and do it with a glad heart. Be optimistic and cheerful; have confidence in yourself and the rightness of your cause. Sometimes friends of Freedom get the reputation of being tired, discouraged complainers and are nearly always defamed as reactionaries. Many situations look bad, but the promise of Freedom gives us the very best of all hopes.

Never go to sleep at night without knowing you have spent 10 or more minutes that day in the service of Christianity and Freedom. If you have not, telephone, asking others to join the 10-minute crusade until you catch up and are on schedule. It may seem you can do nothing in 10 minutes, but when millions of us pursue this crusade there will be 20 million hours per day devoted to this great cause, a force for Freedom which atheism and Communism cannot overcome.

Ask gifted friends to write letters to the Editor of 150 words or less taking a pro-Freedom stand on neglected subjects. The side using the truth has great advantage in the forum debate, which is the most widely read of anything back of the front page. Letters are available for review 15 minutes or 15 days later. Commend the writers of good letters and commend the newspaper for publishing them. Patriots sometimes complain of "managed news," but the letterwriter can "manage" the news he creates. He will reach public officials if his letter is published and can send copies of all letters he has written editors. If a paper fails to publish his letter, the officials will learn which side the paper is on. If he will cause 3 or 4 friends to sign their name and address on a copy of the letter beneath his signature and a "note," reading: "I approve of the above," the copy of his letter to the editor becomes a short petition, which is the most effective of any petition.

Form acquaintances with patriotic members of the communications media. Nearly every publication and radio or television station has at least one active patriot on its staff. Find, encourage, and befriend them. They may often feel alone and helpless. Let them know that you are for them. Mail clippings to writers which will be helpful to them in preparing editorials, and alert them to news developments which constitute good news for the cause of liberty. Byline writers on any subject have a part in forming public opinion and are good people for a Freedom advocate to know.

The press has the facilities and capabilities in its personnel to save its freedom. In trying to save freedom of the press, it will save many other freedoms vital to the continuance of our Republic. With the present trend in the United States, people of the press may find it important to save its very existence and their chosen vocation.

For each 100,000 population in the U.S., there is one daily paper published. In Communist countries the nearest approach to this U.S. ratio is Czechoslovakia, where 7 times as many people are required to support a daily; in Rumania, 14 times as many; in the Soviet Union, 47 times as many; and in Red China, 850 times as many as in the U.S.A.

These statistics are seldom published, but newspapermen are aware of them. Nevertheless, they are inclined to discredit and condemn patriots who oppose communism and are dedicated to the Constitution which is the lifeline of our Republic. Newsmen could have no better friends than patriots, for their jobs are dependent on a high percent of patriots. Some of them may not yet understand the difference between a Republic and a democracy.

Patronize and support the shows of producers who never

put anything in their shows that would discredit immortals of American history or heroes of the present, and commend both the producers and theaters carrying these shows. The shows which carry sly lines or scenes that discredit the American way of life should never be supported by the Liberty Legions. The same is true of TV and radio.

Liberty Legions must not take time out from their great mission for any bitterness and hate. "Hate" belongs to the enemies which assail them. They use it effectively, but let them have it. Freedomists must rely on truth and reason.

Encourage young people to avoid filthy reading material and to read wholesome publications. Keep a careful watch on required and recommended reading matter at your school and help circulate good material. Help arrange essay and speaking contests on patriotic themes.

Find out how you can help cut down juvenile delinquency and build up active patriotism together with an ennobling way of life among our young people. Work through your school, Sunday School, Church, or any constructive youth group. Young people are fun and will keep you young.

The following books by H. L. Hunt may be ordered postpaid from LIFE LINE, Dallas, Tex. 75206:

WHY NOT SPEAK,
    192 pages, soft-cover . . . $ .75

FABIANS FIGHT FREEDOM,
    192 pages, soft-cover 75

HUNT FOR TRUTH,
    254 pages, soft-cover 95

H L H COLUMNS,
    192 pages, soft-cover 75

JULIE BENELL'S FAVORITE
RECIPES, (Published by
H L H Products) 3.95

"PLAYBOY" Interview . . .   .25, 5 for $1.00

RIGHT OF AVERAGE,
    192 pages, soft-cover . . .   .75 Delivery Nov. 1, 1967

ALPACA REVISITED,
    192 pages . . . . 4.00 Delivery Oct. 17, 1967

ALPACA REVISITED,
    224 pages, soft-cover . . . 1.00 Delivery Oct. 24, 1967

HUNT HOME STYLED AFTER MT. VERNON